THE WONDER OF WATER

THE WONDER OF WATER

WATER'S PROFOUND FITNESS FOR LIFE ON EARTH AND MANKIND

MICHAEL DENTON

SEATTLE   DISCOVERY INSTITUTE PRESS   2017

Description

From roaring waterfalls and crashing waves to gentle rain and billowing clouds, water pervades our planet's majestic biosphere. It is easy to take for granted. But this ever-present substance is amazingly fit in a myriad of ways to sustain life on Earth, especially human life. Its unique properties allow it to fill many roles throughout the biological world, from forming the matrix of our cells, to regulating the temperature of our planet.

In *The Wonder of Water*, biologist Michael Denton delves deep into this grand, untold story and explores how water is specially equipped to allow life to flourish on our blue planet. Find more information on The Privileged Species book series and companion documentaries at www. WonderofWater.org.

Library Cataloging Data

The Wonder of Water: Water's Profound Fitness for Life on Earth and Mankind by Michael Denton

All charts (unless otherwise noted) by Brian Gage.

226 pages, 6 x 9 x 0.5 in. & 0.7 lb, 229 x 152 x 12 mm & x 309 g

Library of Congress Control Number: 2017952451

SCI086000 SCIENCE / Life Sciences / General

SCI009000 SCIENCE / Life Sciences / Biophysics

SCI008000 SCIENCE / Life Sciences / Biology

ISBN-13: 978-1-936599-47-9 (paperback), 978-1-936599-49-3 (Kindle), 978-1-936599-48-6 (EPUB)

Publisher Information

Discovery Institute Press, 208 Columbia Street, Seattle, WA 98104

Internet: http://www. discoveryinstitutepress.org/

Published in the United States of America on acid-free paper.

First Edition: October 2017.

Contents

Acknowledgments 9

Before the Bridalveil Fall 11

1. The Water Wheel 15

2. Tectonic Recycling 35

3. Preserving the Ocean 61

4. The Climate Machine 87

5. Water, Trees, and Light 105

6. Water and Human Physiology 123

7. Water and the Cell 157

8. Conclusion 179

Endnotes 189

Image Credits 219

Index 223

ACKNOWLEDGMENTS

THE EVIDENCE CITED IN THE MONOGRAPH IS DRAWN FROM A NUMber of sources. These include many of the papers and articles of Philip Ball, including his lucid book *H$_2$O: A Biography of Water*; Marcia Bjornerud's equally lucid and wonderfully written *Reading the Rocks*; Tom Garrison's *Oceanography: An Invitation to Marine Science*; Nick Rogers et al.'s *Introduction to our Dynamic Planet*; Geoffrey Vallis's *Climate and the Oceans*; James Lovelock's *Gaia: A New Look at Life on Earth*; Lenton and Watson's *Revolutions that Made the Earth*; Steven Vogel's *Comparative Biomechanics*; Schmidt-Nielsen's books *Animal Physiology* and *Scaling*; and Gerald Pollack et al.'s *Water and the Cell*. Many aspects of fitness discussed here were first highlighted by Lawrence Henderson in his classic *The Fitness of the Environment*, by Arthur Needham in his *The Uniqueness of Biological Materials*, and in the many publications of George Wald and Harold Morowitz.

I would also like to thank Jonathan Kopel, Tyler Hampton, and Ian George Johnston for critical reading of a very preliminary draft and suggesting many important clarifications and improvements. I would also like to thank the staff of the Discovery Institute, especially John West, Jonathan Witt, Guillermo Gonzalez, Jonathan Wells, and Rachel Adams for critical reading and editing of the text. Without their commitment and efforts the book could never have seen the light of day.

BEFORE THE
BRIDALVEIL FALL

SUMMER IN YOSEMITE. STANDING UNDERNEATH THE BRIDALVEIL Fall, the spray gently sprinkles your face and diffracts the sunlight into a rainbow. The scene in the valley is one of stunning beauty. The sensual symphony of the scene intoxicates; the sound of the falling water, the sweet aroma of the conifers and scents of summer in the air; the feel of the sunlight on your skin, and the sheer visual delight in the beauty of the surroundings; the sheer ice carved cliffs and the green of the valley floor. We are entranced in a silent reverie at the wondrous harmony of the scene.

Curiously, however, the wonder we *do* perceive when we visit Yosemite and stand spellbound under the Fall is only a part of the story. There is another hidden, vital wonder in the scene, which is every bit as wondrous as the vision of the sunlight on the falling waters. It is far less familiar, but it makes possible our standing before the Fall and our appreciation of her beauty; it is a wonder that unites us to the waterfall in ways unimagined.

Those tumbling waters, and indeed those of every waterfall on Earth, are hard at work eroding the rocks. By this primal activity, ongoing for billions of years, the waters tumbling over a myriad of falls in every region of Earth are playing a key role in leaching minerals from the rocks. Through this process, water provides the vital elements of life for all land-based creatures. Without this vital work, performed before our eyes as these beautiful cascading waters fall to the valley floor, there would be no essential elements and nutrients for life on land. The world would be a barren waste. No one would ever gaze upon the beauty of Yosemite.

As we contemplate the beauty of the fall, yet another unseen and very different magic is at work inside our bodies. This one also depends on the unique fitness of water, and it too makes it possible, though in a far more immediate and intimate sense, for us to perceive the scene. The same wonder substance that is eroding those rocks and providing life with essential nutrients and minerals *is* doing something else! By virtue of another suite of unique chemical and physical properties, talents very different from those it uses in the fall, water provides us and all complex life on earth with an ideal medium for a circulatory system. With each beat of our heart, water carries to our tissues oxygen and many of those very same nutrients leached from the rocks in the fall. Water also ferries away the waste products of respiration—carbon dioxide to the lungs, other waste products to the kidneys, and excess heat to the skin, where it is vented from the body.

Our vital dependence on those beautiful tumbling waters for the life-giving minerals she draws from the rocks *and* our equally vital dependence on the water coursing through our arteries carrying many of those same elements around the body brings us face to face with a revelation as extraordinary as any other in any domain of science. The one substance, water, is uniquely fit to serve two utterly different vital ends—ends as different as can be conceived: the erosion of rock and the circulation of the blood. Both are absolutely vital to our existence. No other substance in nature comes close to having the essential set of properties needed to do these two jobs.

If water served only these two very different vital ends, it would be miracle enough. But as we shall also see in the chapters ahead, water's unique fitness for life on Earth involves a vast ensemble of additional elements of fitness serving a vast inventory of diverse vital ends. These include the formation of the Earth itself, formation of the oceans, climate moderation and the hydrological cycle, tectonic plate movement, continent formation, and photosynthesis. The unique properties of water are also needed to make soil, cool the human body, fold proteins, and form cell membranes. Water enables phenomena and processes that unfold on vastly different spatial and temporal scales, from thousands of kilometers and millions of years down to nanometers and milliseconds.

The purpose of this book is to tell the untold story of water's vast web of unique and diverse properties, properties that are indispensable for terrestrial life. The chapters ahead show that these many properties reveal a transcendent *biocentric* unity in the fabric of nature. They reveal that life on Earth—including humankind—is not mere cosmic happenstance. Through its magic, water sings a universal song of life, and in its special fitness for human physiology it sings a special song of man. The properties of water show that beings with our biology do indeed occupy a special central place in the order of nature, and that the blueprint for life was present in the properties of matter from the moment of creation. We may have been displaced from the spatial center of the universe but not its "teleological center." In the properties of water the so-called "Copernican Principle" is well and truly overturned.

1. The Water Wheel

For is not the whole Substance of all Vegetables mere modified Water? and consequently of all Animals too; all of which either feed upon Vegetables or prey upon one another? Is not an immense quantity of it continually exhaled by the Sun, to fill the atmosphere with Vapors and Clouds, and feed the Plants of the Earth with the balm of Dews... It seems incredible at first hearing, that all the Blood in our Bodies should circulate in a trice, in a very few minutes: but I believe it would be more surprising, if we knew the short and swift periods of the great Circulation of Water, that vital Blood of the Earth, which composeth and nourisheth all things.
Richard Bentley, *Confutation of Atheism from the Frame of the World* (1693)[1]

ALTHOUGH WATER IS ONE OF THE MOST FAMILIAR OF ALL SUBstances, its remarkable nature never fails to impress. As a liquid, it accumulates on the Earth's surface, from great oceans to small lakes and tiny puddles. In motion, it may swirl violently down a great cataract, or flow serenely as a mature river meandering across a flood plain. On the surface of large bodies of water, the wind pushes up waves both great and small, from the booming surf of Hawaii to the ripples on a garden pond. Tiny droplets of the substance form the matrix of the clouds. Slightly larger drops fall through the atmosphere from the clouds to the ground as rain.

As a solid, it falls as snow, creating frosted patterns on the windowpane in winter and forming the great ice sheets of the polar regions and the valley glaciers in the mountains. In the higher latitudes, water forms the entire scenery of the landscape: the ice caps at the fringes of the polar continents; the icebergs floating in the restless gray and ice-cold sea; the spray carried from wave tops by the wind, frozen instantly into tiny pellets of ice in the sub-zero temperatures and splattered like shrapnel onto the nearby ice shelves.

FIGURE 1.1. WATER PICTURED IN THREE FORMS—LIQUID, SOLID (ICE) AND A GAS (WATER VAPOR). CLOUDS ARE CLUSTERS OF WATER DROPLETS CONDENSED FROM WATER VAPOR.

The sounds of water are no less diverse. There is the rhythmic pounding of the surf, the deafening roar of a great waterfall, the babbling of a mountain brook, the gentle patter of summer rain, the clatter of hail against an iron roof, the grinding booms and sharp reports of an advancing glacier, and the thunder of an avalanche.[2]

No other single substance comes close to providing such drama, clothing Earth with such a dazzling kaleidoscope of exotic and beautiful forms.

Three Material States

WATER'S UNIQUE diversity of forms, from waterfalls to icicles, is due to a unique and fascinating property: Water can exist as a solid, liquid, and gas in the ambient conditions that exist on the surface of the Earth. All other natural substances on Earth—including the various mineral constituents of the rocks and the gases of the atmosphere—exist only as one form of matter in ambient conditions. As Philip Ball comments, "Almost all of the non-aqueous fabric of our planet remains in the same physical state. The oxygen and nitrogen of the air do not condense; the rock, sands, and soils do not melt... or evaporate."[3]

It is only in the deep Earth that particular substances other than water may exist in more than one form. Rocks may melt into liquids or remain solid depending on their distance from the Earth's center, where heat and pressure effects are very different from those familiar on the surface. Substances that are gaseous in the atmosphere may be liquid or solid in the extreme physical conditions in parts of the Earth's mantle and core.[4] The core itself, as is well known, consists partly of molten iron. But within the range of temperatures and atmospheric pressures that exist on the Earth's surface, only water exists as solid, liquid, and gas.[5]

Water has a low molecular weight (MW) of 18. However, compared to other "low molecule weight" compounds its boiling and melting points are far higher. The following light molecular compounds are typical in that they are all gases at room temperature: carbon dioxide, CO_2 (MW=44); Oxygen, O_2 (MW=32); Carbon monoxide, CO (MW=28); Nitrogen, N_2 (MW=28); Methane, CH_4 (MW=16). None are solids at 0°C. At one atmospheric pressure water melts at 0°C and boils at 100°C. Ammonia, NH_3 (MW=17) has a molecular weight similar to water, but melts at –78°C and boils at –33°C.

Albert Szent-Györgyi was struck by water's highly anomalous behavior in this regard:

> The extraordinary nature of water is borne out by the two constants used most frequently for the characterization of substances: melting and boiling points. According to the size of its molecules, water should boil at 0°C. It boils at 100°C. It should melt at –100°C. It melts at 0°C, indicating that water molecules tend to stick together. We have to decrease the temperature only by 1/273, cooling it from 273°K to 272°K, and water turns into a solid which can split rocks. Eskimos build their houses with it.[6]

Water has such anomalously high melting and boiling points because individual molecules of water form a unique, extended, cohesive (sticky) hydrogen-bonded network—causing what Szent-Györgyi calls their tendency "to stick together." A brief account of water's hydrogen-bonded network is given in Chapter 7.

The Great Wheel

WATER'S UNIQUE property of existing in all three states within the ambient temperatures on Earth has one consequence of great importance, particularly for terrestrial life. It confers on water a unique fitness for one of the most important processes on the planet: the hydrological or water cycle. This cycle provides water for terrestrial ecosystems and makes life on land possible. As Philip Ball comments, "The very existence of a hydrological cycle is a consequence of water's unique ability to exist in more than one physical state—solid, liquid, or gas—under the conditions that prevail at the surface of the planet."[7] Of all known substances, only water is fit for the hydrological cycle, the delivery system of water to land-based life.

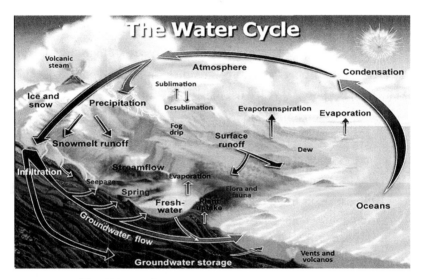

FIGURE 1.2. THE WATER CYCLE.

Everyone learns of the hydrological cycle at school. Water evaporates from the sea, rises into the atmosphere, cools, and eventually condenses into tiny droplets forming clouds. These coalesce into larger droplets and fall to the ground as rain or snow. Unmelted snow forms glaciers (in higher latitudes), and water from rain and melting snow drains into rivers—one way or the other returning to the sea, where the process begins again. The scale of the cycle is remarkable, as Ball points out:

> Each 3100 years, a volume of water equivalent to all the oceans pass-es through the atmosphere, carried there by evaporation and moved by precipitation… the Sun's heat removes from the oceans the equiv-alent of three feet in depth each year—875 cubic kilometers in total every day.[8]

Remarkable though the cycle is, its exceptional nature is seldom acknowledged. As Ball comments, "This cycle of evaporation and con-densation has come to seem so perfectly natural that we never think to remark on why no other substances display such transformations."[9]

Water's unique ability to exist in three different states in ambient conditions is a necessary condition for the hydrological wheel, but the cycle also depends on other unique properties of water. The wheel has kept on turning for billions of years only because liquid water and global temperatures have been conserved by regulatory mechanisms—many of which also depend on unique properties of water and are discussed in Chapter 3.

Two more properties of water essential to the turning of the hydro-logical wheel are water's relatively low viscosity, and the relatively high mobility of liquid water compared with other fluids and of ice compared with many crystalline solids.

The viscosities of fluids and solids vary greatly over many orders of magnitude.[10] Were the viscosities of ice and water much greater, all the water on Earth would accumulate in vast immobile beds of ice cover-ing the higher latitudes, the great continental landmasses would be cov-ered in varying thicknesses of viscous "water," and the hydrological cycle would grind to a halt.

In effect, the hydrological cycle is enabled not by one unique property of water, but by several properties that "conspire together," as it were, to turn the "wheel" and provide water for land-based life.

Without the hydrological cycle the entire land surface of Earth would be a dehydrated, lifeless waste, more lifeless than the Atacama or any of the most dehydrated deserts currently on Earth. Although the importance of the hydrological cycle is widely acknowledged, what is, as far as I am aware, never mentioned is the remarkable fact that the delivery of water to the land, an essential medium of all life on Earth, is in effect carried out by and dependent on the properties of water itself, unaided by any other external regulatory systems.

In this extraordinary fact we glimpse the first example of what may only be described as the transcending fitness of water for life as it exists on Earth. Contrast this with our own artifactual designs, where key commodities such as gasoline or food or clothes can only be delivered to where they are needed by extraneous delivery systems like trains and trucks. Gasoline will not transport and deliver itself to filling stations, nor clothes to shopping malls. But the delivery of water to terrestrial ecosystems depends almost entirely on the intrinsic properties of water itself.

Erosion and Weathering

WHILE THE hydrological cycle delivers an endless supply of water to the land, making terrestrial life and ecosystems possible, and this might perhaps be considered its primary function, it does much more than this. Inevitably as the wheel turns it performs another major task critical to all terrestrial life. The tumbling waters of a million mountain streams, coursing over the exposed lithosphere, continually leach minerals from the rocks and enrich and replenish all the waters of the terrestrial hydrosphere, including lakes, rivers, subsurface ground waters, soil, wet lands, etc., with the vital elements of life which are essential to all living things on Earth.

But what is really extraordinary about this second great function of the water wheel—that of delivering the minerals of life to terrestrial life—is the way in which a suite of diverse properties of water "conspire intelligently" together to carry out the task of eroding and weathering the rocks. And again it is via the properties of water itself—this time a suite of diverse chemical and physical properties—which "working together" achieve this second great life-giving end.

The Alkahest: It is hard to conceive of a more ideal agent than water for dissolving the vital minerals in the Earth's crust. As the *alkahest* (the supreme solvent) of the alchemists, water is uniquely fit for this task. This has been acknowledged for many years. In his classic *The Fitness of the Environment,* Lawrence Joseph Henderson alludes to its geological role in weathering the rocks as evidence of its great solvation powers: "Under the action of water, aided, to be sure, in many cases by dissolved carbonic acid, every species of rock suffers slow destruction. All substances yield *in situ* to the solvent work of water."[11]

Henderson cites as evidence of its power the vast amount of materials carried to the sea by all the rivers of the Earth in one year, an estimated five thousand million tons of dissolved mineral matter.[12] As the late Felix Franks, perhaps the leading modern authority on water, put it, "The almost universal solvent action of liquid water… [makes] its rigorous purification extremely difficult. Nearly all known chemicals dissolve in water to a slight, but detectable extent."[13]

Although the hydrological cycle also provides mineral replenishment for the oceans as the rivers carrying a significant fraction of the minerals leached from the rocks eventually run into the sea, the oceans have another source of minerals; from the upwelling of the molten magma from the mantle in the mid oceanic ridges and hydrothermal vents. See discussion in Chapter 2.

Water's ability to weather and dissolve rocks is greatly enhanced and hastened by two of its other properties: (1) carbon dioxide (CO_2) is soluble in water; (2) carbon dioxide reacts with water to produce a mild acid, carbonic acid, which promotes many chemical reactions with the minerals in rocks and helps dissolve them. Two such chemical reactions are shown below:

$$H_2CO_3 + CaCO_3 \longrightarrow Ca(HCO_3)_2$$

Carbonic acid + calcium carbonate $\longrightarrow$ calcium bicarbonate

$$Mg_2SiO_4 + 4\,CO_2 + 4\,H_2O \rightleftharpoons 2\,Mg^{2+} + 4\,HCO_{3-} + H_4SiO_4$$

olivine + carbon dioxide + water $\rightleftharpoons$ Magnesium ions
and bicarbonate ions in solution + silicic acid in solution

Surface Tension and Expansion on Freezing: Two other unique properties of water that play an important role in erosion and weathering
are water's high surface tension (after mercury, the second highest of
any common liquid) and its anomalous expansion on freezing. Water is
drawn into rock fissures by its high surface tension and then subsequent-
ly expands on freezing. The expansion is about ten percent in terms of
volume, and it exerts tremendous pressure on the surrounding rocks,
breaking them apart and presenting a greater surface area for chemical
weathering. The expansion of water on freezing is again, like its existence
in three states in ambient conditions, another anomalous and practically
unique property of water. Only one other known substance, the metal
gallium, expands on freezing in the ambient temperature range (26°C).[14]
Here is another property of water which is unique in the ambient temperature range along with its existence as liquid, gas, and solid.

Viscosity: Water's low viscosity and mobility as it tumbles over cataracts and courses down river valleys on its way to the sea, in conjunction with the abrasive action of the tiny rock particles carried within the
stream, further enhances water's erosional powers. Working as a sort of
liquid sandpaper, it carves out valleys, gorges, and ravines, and dumps
into deltas, lakes, and seas.

As alluded to above, the viscosity of substances varies over many orders of magnitude. The viscosity of nitrogen is extremely low: 0.0000167
Pa-s. (Pa-s stands for Pascal-seconds, the standard unit for viscosity
measurements.) Water's viscosity is 0.001 Pa-s. The viscosity of canola
oil is 0.033 Pa-s; motor oil 0.2 Pa-s; tar, 30,000 Pa-s[15]; and crustal rocks,
between 10^{21} and 10^{24} Pa-s.[16] Within this vast range of values the viscosity of water must be very close to what it is or its erosional capacity would
be vastly diminished. If the viscosity of water were higher, closer to that
of many other liquids—olive oil, for example—its mobility and ability

to abrade rocks would be much reduced. Think of honey flowing over a rock! Moreover given a more viscous "water," vast areas of the Earth's land surface would drain only very slowly, leaving enormous swaths covered in a sticky quagmire. Land life, if any could even exist on such an inclement counterfactual world, would be acutely challenged. Or again, if water's viscosity were appreciably lower (like that of a gas), its mobility would be greater but its ability to carry abrasive particles would be less.

Working together, the various properties of water involved in erosion and weathering are extraordinarily efficient, and they wear away immense quantities of rock in remarkably short periods of time. Dramatic evidence of water's erosional power is seen in the fact that the Niagara Falls has retreated about seven miles upstream in only about 12,000 years.[17]

Glaciers: It is not just the precise viscosity and mobility of liquid water that makes it so fit for eroding rocks. The viscosity of solid water, ice, also plays a part. First, the viscosity of ice is actually very low for a crystalline solid. The viscosity of the rocks in the Earth's crust is between 10^{21} and 10^{24} Pa-s. The viscosity of ice in a glacier is only about 10^{11} Pa-s,[18] about ten orders of magnitude lower. As mentioned above, if the viscosity of ice had been closer to the viscosity of rock, all the waters of Earth would be locked up in vast immobile ice caps at the poles and in high mountain regions. Arguably, there might be very little liquid water on Earth. But it would also mean that ice would be unable to play a key role in the erosion of rocks. To erode rocks, it must be mobile at least to some degree.

Even so, the movement of glaciers would be much slower if it were not for the pressure of the overlying ice, which lowers its viscosity and converts ice deeper than fifty meters from a brittle solid into something that behaves much more like a viscous fluid, a condition in which it becomes subject to plastic flow.[19]

Curiously, liquid water also greatly assists in the speeding up of glacial flow by a process known as basal sliding.[20] This is where the glacier slides over a layer of liquid water. The same phenomenon is at work on an ice rink, where the skater's blade glides across the surface of ice because the pressure of the blade produces a film of water between it and the surface of the ice. Similarly, water that melts under the high pressure at the base of a glacier greatly reduces the friction of the ice on the ground beneath it. It is remarkable not only that the pressure of ice above softens the ice below, rendering it more plastic and mobile, but also that the pressure produces liquid water to assist glacial movement. Water *as a liquid*, in other words, hastens the flow of water *as a solid*!

Mineral-laden glaciers humble the hardest mountain rock, carrying vast stores of material into flood plains and oceans. As glaciers flow down river valleys or across great continental land masses, sliding over the bedrock, they drag along rocks and rock fragments across the underlying surface, grinding away the underlying rocks and reducing them to "rock flour," material made up of tiny grains of rock, fractions of a millimeter in size. This greatly increases the area available for chemical weathering. Glacial erosion leads to classic alpine scenery—U shaped valleys, hanging valleys, terraces, and terminal moraines.

In sum: Water is uniquely fit for its role in eroding and weathering rocks thanks to a remarkable suite of diverse properties, many of them unique and anomalous, which act together to the grand and vital end of carrying essential nutrients to terrestrial life. And this synergy is possible in turn only because of the prior fitness of water to enable the hydrological cycle.

Soil

WHILE THE hydrological cycle provides both water and the necessary minerals for terrestrial life, there is still another condition that must be satisfied if land-based life is to thrive. The water enriched with the vital nutrients of life must be retained in the soil, to provide an accessible and long-term supply of water and nutrients for absorption by the roots of land plants. Amazingly, the inevitable end of water's work in eroding and weathering the rocks—the same process which yields the harvest of nutrients that fertilizes and enables land-based life—*also* results in the

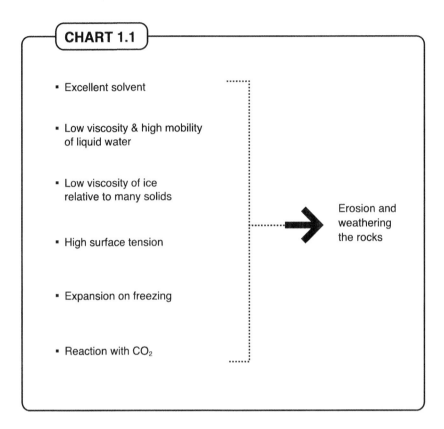

CHART 1.1

- Excellent solvent

- Low viscosity & high mobility of liquid water

- Low viscosity of ice relative to many solids

- High surface tension

- Expansion on freezing

- Reaction with CO_2

Erosion and weathering the rocks

formation of a set of mineral components that together make up an ideal matrix for retaining water and its cargo of dissolved mineral nutrients.

This matrix includes a variety of sands (grain size is greater than sixty-three microns) and silts (between two and sixty-three microns) and various types of clay (particle size under two microns), which comes from the chemical weathering of silicates. This mix of non-organic matter in the soils provides a vast surface area and a labyrinth of micropores in which water is retained by capillary action. Such water is often termed *capillary water* in contrast to *gravitational water*. The latter resides in macro-pores and can drain rapidly from the soil. Capillary water hangs around for much longer, a nice trick to help a region's plants through the next dry spell. In fact, the water-retaining property of soils is crucial to the survival of plants. As leading soil scientists Nyle Brady and Raymond Weil comment:

> As long as plant leaves are exposed to sunlight, the plant requires a continuous stream of water to use in cooling, nutrient transport, turgor maintenance, and photosynthesis. Because plants use water continuously, but in most places it rains only occasionally, the water-holding capacity of soils is essential for plant survival. A deep soil may store enough water to allow plants to survive long periods without rain.[21] [Such as Acacia trees on the African savannah which may go without water for almost five months.[22]]

It is easy to imagine the dire consequences for plant life if soils only contained macropores through which water could drain quickly away, or, alternatively, if soils were impermeable. After only one week without rain, the majority of plants would begin to wither and die. If soil were impermeable, then as Brady and Weil comment, "Most of the rain could not penetrate the soil, but... [would run] off the hillsides on the soil surface, scouring surface soil and debris as it picked up speed, and entering the river rapidly and nearly all at once. The result would be a destructive flash flood."[23] And over time, the result would be the de-vegetation and desertification of Earth's land surface. In effect, the land surface would be as bereft of vegetation as the Atacama Desert.

Clay: Clay makes one of the most significant contributions to the water- and ion-retaining properties of soil. Clay is a fine-grained component of most soils and consists largely of clay minerals along with some metal oxides and organic matter. Clay minerals are hydrous silicates or aluminosilicates.

This water and ion-absorbing characteristic of clay resides in its unique layered micro-structure—like the pages of a book—where each page consists basically of a layer of silicon and oxygen atoms. These atoms carry charges that attract other charged atoms or molecules (ions) and water so that the whole structure acts as a great reservoir that holds ions in the soil and prevents their being leached out by water as it percolates through the soil. All of this is greatly aided by the enormous surface area of the clay particles. As Brady and Weil point out, "The external surface area of 1 gram of colloidal clay is at least 1,000 times that of coarse sand."[24] And as they further note, "Next to photosynthesis and respiration, probably no process in nature is as vital to plant life as the exchange of ions between soil particles and growing plant roots."[25] This exchange process "joins photosynthesis as a fundamental life-supporting process," they continue. "Without this property of soils terrestrial ecosystems would not be able to retain sufficient nutrients to support natural or introduced vegetation."[26]

Were it not for the almost universal occurrence of clay minerals in soil, there would probably be far fewer large terrestrial plants on Earth and perhaps no large terrestrial mammals.

There is a beautiful and elegant teleology in all this. The same process which draws from rocks the minerals and essential elements for life generates at the same time—in the clays and sands and silts that together form soil with organic debris—an ideal water- and mineral-retaining matrix that provides the means by which the mineral-enriched water can be used by plants. (And also ultimately by animals, because in a sense plants are nature's intermediaries, a means of imbibing and concentrating the minerals eroded from the rocks and transmitting them to the

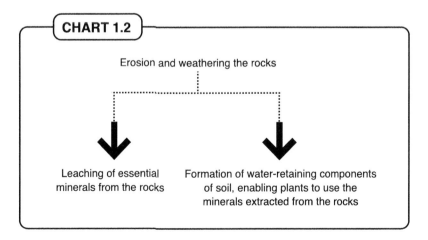

CHART 1.2

Erosion and weathering the rocks

Leaching of essential minerals from the rocks

Formation of water-retaining components of soil, enabling plants to use the minerals extracted from the rocks

terrestrial herbivores that feed on them, and to the carnivores that feed on the herbivores.)

It is further evidence of nature's unique fitness for life on Earth that clay particles, which are a major component of most soils and play such an important role in promoting vegetative growth, are the inevitable end of the erosion and weathering by water of silicate rock. In a real sense, our existence as terrestrial life forms depends on the fact that the most common crustal rocks, the silicates, weather to what appears to be an ideal material for plant life, absorbing both water and the essential nutrients needed for plant growth.

And there is yet another teleological aspect of this: Silicates make up the bulk of the lithosphere, ensuring that weathering throughout the terrestrial realm results in clay minerals that promote water retention in soil and the growth of plants. Yet another teleological aspect is the fact that the weathering of silicate rock provides a means of controlling global temperatures (as described in more detail in Chapter 3), and through the controlling of global temperatures, the preserving of liquid water on Earth—an essential precondition for the hydrological cycle itself and ultimately the formation of clays.

There is another intriguing teleological twist to this unfolding tale, that one unique property of water—its high surface tension—plays an

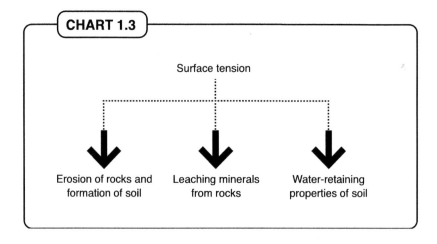

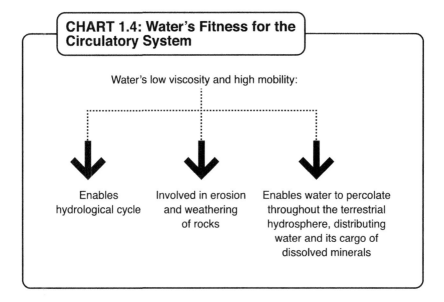

CHART 1.4: Water's Fitness for the Circulatory System

Water's low viscosity and high mobility:

| Enables hydrological cycle | Involved in erosion and weathering of rocks | Enables water to percolate throughout the terrestrial hydrosphere, distributing water and its cargo of dissolved minerals |

important role in the erosional process, enhancing water's ability to leach minerals from rocks, and as the major physical force which stores water in the micropores of sand and silt and clay.

Water's low viscosity and consequent high mobility also enables it to "circulate" through the ground waters and micropores in the soils, delivering water (itself!) and its vital harvest of dissolved minerals to soils and ground waters throughout the terrestrial domain. And the delivery of such a harvest of minerals is of course dependent not only on water's mobility but on its great solvation powers. Water is, as Ball points out, both a "superb solvent" and in "constant flux."[27] Its mobility enables it to percolate through the soils in every corner of the terrestrial hydrosphere, and its solvation powers enable it to carry its mineral harvest to every terrestrial ecosystem. So water not only leaches minerals from the rocks, but it also distributes by its own powers the vital building blocks of life to the soils throughout the terrestrial hydrosphere, enabling flowers to bloom, trees to grow, and animal life to exist.

Providence

THE CONCEPTION of a global hydrological cycle, with water evaporating from the seas, condensing to form clouds, falling as rain on the land, and returning to the sea via streams and rivers to complete the circuit, dates back more than 2,000 years. As James Dooge writes:

> Anaximander (c. 570 B.C.)... described the cause and the movement of water from sea to sky as evaporation, one of the key elements of the hydrological cycle. Xenophanes of Colophon (c. 530 B.C.) added the concepts of water transport by clouds and the production of rainfall from clouds to feed springs and rivers. Anaxagoras of Clazomenae (c. 460 B.C.) asserted that the various water processes constituted a closed cycle involving both movement and storage. Diogenes of Apollonia (460–390 B.C.) contended that fresh water evaporated from the sea and later fed the rivers in the form of rain. Plato (c. 390 B.C.) reviewed the work of his predecessors and added the concept of percolation.[28]

For many centuries, through the medieval and early modern periods, many authors held to the misconception that rainfall in itself is insufficient to account for the flow of water in rivers, and they believed that the rest was provided by underground channels that conveyed water upward from the sea to springs and the source of streams. Leonardo da Vinci pictured the process as being analogous to the rise of water in the stems and veins of plants: "The raising of the water to the mountains... acts like water that raises up through plants to the summits, as seen in vines when they are cut; and as the blood works in all animals so water does in the world, which is a living animal."[29]

But from the early seventeenth century, rainfall was increasingly acknowledged to be sufficient to supply the streams and rivers with water. This was conclusively demonstrated by the chemist John Dalton in a celebrated paper he read to the Manchester Literary and Philosophical society in 1799.[30] According to geographer Yi-Fu Tuan, Dalton asserted that the fitness of this great cycle for life on Earth and especially its ensuring that terrestrial regions receive an endless supply of water is relatively self-evident and was one of the first elements of natural fitness alluded to as evidence of providence.[31] In the opening remarks of his paper (as reported by Tuan), "Dalton could not refrain from expressing again his admiration for the beautiful system of nature and for the provident, unceasing circulation of water."[32]

But before Dalton, the water cycle had long been a source of wonderment and a popular topic of natural theology. John Ray, in his *Wisdom of God Manifest in the Works of Creation*, saw in the distribution of clouds and rain "a great Argument of Providence and Divine disposition."[33] And he saw as providential the delivery of water to the land via gentle drops of rain rather than a destructive stream which "would gall the Ground, wash away Plants by the roots, overthrow Houses, and greatly incommode, if not suffocate Animals."[34] Ray also saw the winds as dissipating "contagious Vapours" and transferring "Clouds from Place to Place, for the more commodious watering of the Earth."[35] As Yi-Fu Tuan points out in his *The Hydrologic Cycle and the Wisdom of God*, from 1700–1850 the concept of the hydrological cycle was the "handmaiden of natural theology as much as it was a child of natural philosophy."[36] Tuan continues:

> Of the three classes of evidence —astronomical, terrestrial and biological—terrestrial evidence proved in some ways to be the most difficult to draw upon in support of the notion of a wise and provident God. Until the concept of the hydrologic cycle was introduced and elaborated, it was difficult to argue convincingly for rationality in the pattern of land and sea, in the existence of mountains, in the occurrence of floods, etc. The hydrologic cycle served as an ordering principle, and when combined with the geologic cycle, it assumed a grandeur of inclusiveness that makes some of our modern efforts to describe the Earth look like a medley of disjointed facts and ideas.[37]

A Teleological Tapestry

IN THIS chapter we have seen that it is the unique capacity of water to exist in the three states of matter in the ambient temperature range, in conjunction with the low viscosity of ice and water, that makes possible the *hydrological cycle*, which has reliably delivered water to the terrestrial ecosystems of planet Earth for millions of years. And because the turning of the hydrological wheel depends largely on the unique properties of water, this means that in effect, water, the very matrix of life, delivers itself to land-based ecosystems by its own capacities. We also have seen that water further possesses just the right suite of diverse chemical and physical properties for the efficient erosion and weathering of the rocks, and for extracting the essential nutrients of life, while at the same time generating the key constituents of the soils that store that vital harvest for the benefit of plant life and indirectly all animal life on land.

In the case of water's erosional and weathering abilities, it is hard to imagine any phenomenon more indicative of design. Here is a diverse set of physical and chemical properties that convey the impression of having been arranged specifically to the end of breaking down rocks both mechanically and chemically. Even if just one property were involved in eroding the rocks it would be wonder enough, especially in conjunction with the fact that the hydrological cycle depends, as discussed above, on the unique capacity of water to exist in multiple states in ambient conditions. But already we have touched on not one but at least five different properties of water that work together in the task of breaking down rocks and weathering minerals: (1) water's ability to exist in three different states in the ambient temperature range; (2) water's high surface tension; (3) water's expansion on freezing; (4) water's viscosity; and (5) water's capacity to dissolve an unusually wide variety of substances.

Perhaps the conspiracy is not the result of design? But certainly the *appearance of design* is highly suggestive, or even "overwhelming"—the term used by Paul Davies in describing the apparent design of the cosmic fine-tuning of the laws of physics for life.[38]

Further, if the precious water and its cargo of dissolved minerals is to be used by land plants, it must be entrapped in some medium and held fast rather than permitted to run quickly to the sea. Again, water comes to the rescue. Because as we saw, the same erosional and weathering processes that provide the minerals for land-based life also inevitably generate a set of material components, including perhaps most importantly various clays, that confer on soil superb water- and mineral-retaining properties, which are vital if those same minerals are to be accessed and used by growing plants.

So the same process that yields the minerals also yields the means for plants to use them. Moreover, one of the properties that assists in the erosion of the rocks and hence in the making of soil—water's high surface tension—is also the key property that holds water in the micropores in the soil, retaining it for use by land plants. And of course all this is a fitness for *land-based life*! Marine plants have no need for water-retaining soil!

Water's properties are fit as delivery man, quarry master, and storekeeper for land-based life, all in one! This is not mere everyday design, analogous to that seen in human technology; this is design of a transcending elegance and parsimony.

The intelligent collusion of various diverse properties of water to serve a particular end such as observed in the erosion and weathering of the rocks, which might be loosely termed "teleology in parallel," is not the only type of teleological pattern of synergic interactions manifest in the unique properties of water for land-based life. This is when one unique property of water—such as water's ability to exist in three states of matter, enabling the hydrological cycle—must be causally prior to the exploitation of a second set of properties—such as those involved in the erosion and weathering of the rocks—which are in turn logically prior to and necessary for a third—such as the water-retaining properties of soil. Such a purposeful use of various elements of fitness in a logical sequence represents what is in effect a teleological hierarchy.

This chapter has highlighted the fact that it is not so much the sheer number of different properties of water fit for life that conveys such an irrepressible sense of design, but the way they work together to achieve ends vital to life on Earth. Yes, the number is impressive; but that fact pales against the deep teleology manifested in their profoundly purposeful synergy. That the pattern of the interactions conforms to a teleological hierarchy is as remarkable a fact as any in the entire realm of science.

And this chapter has also highlighted another aspect of water's fitness: that the fitness of water for life extends far beyond the mere provision of an ideal matrix for the biochemistry of the carbon-based cell. And the extent of water's fitness for life, which has been the focus of this chapter, has shown that many properties of water are uniquely and specifically fit for land-based life on a planet somewhat similar to the Earth. In the fitness of water to turn the great hydrological wheel, to erode mountains, and to provide the minerals of life for land-based organisms, we see clear evidence that water is fit for processes as remote from each other as the erosion of an Andean mountain is from the functioning of a red blood cell.

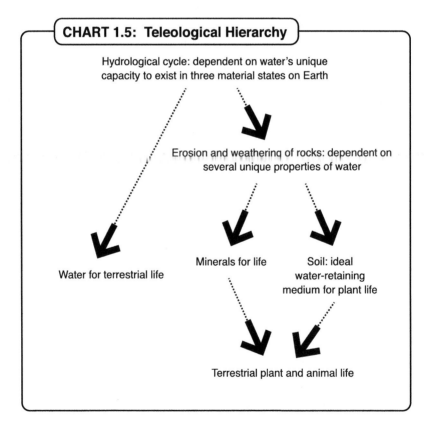

CHART 1.5: Teleological Hierarchy

Hydrological cycle: dependent on water's unique capacity to exist in three material states on Earth

Erosion and weathering of rocks: dependent on several unique properties of water

Water for terrestrial life

Minerals for life

Soil: ideal water-retaining medium for plant life

Terrestrial plant and animal life

2. Tectonic Recycling

Water even in very small quantities influences dramatically a variety of physical and chemical properties of geological materials such as melting temperatures, melt chemistry, viscosity and density, phase equilibria, and reaction kinetics. Therefore water affects fundamental magmatic processes ranging from anatexis [melting] to magma ascent, and crystallization to eruption. Migration of granitic anatectic magmas is the main process of crustal differentiation controlling the thermal and chemical structure of continents... and ultimately the origin of continents.
Roberto Weinberg and Pavlina Hasalová, *Lithos* (January 2015)[1]

H_2O is a critical component of the whole Earth; not just the hydrosphere, but also the crust and the mantle. It controls many aspects of melting, the dominant process of Earth differentiation, and is cycled from the interior of the Earth to the outer layers and back into the interior. The amount of H_2O hidden in the Earth's interior may well be the equivalent to the water in the oceans, despite the outgassing associated with melting and volcanism at the Earth's surface, and the oceans now appear to have been a feature of the Earth from Hadean times onwards.
Nick Rogers, Stephen Blake, Kevin Burton, and Mike Widdowson, *An Introduction to Our Dynamic Planet* (2008)[2]

THE EROSION OF THE NIAGARA GORGE—SEVEN MILES IN 12,000 years—reveals the enormous power and rate of water erosion. The erosion of mountains by water and ice has been estimated to be as high in some regions as two to ten millimeters per year.[3] Ten millimeters per year might not seem much, but in five million years it would wear away 50,000,000 millimeters or 50,000 meters of rock, a height many times more than the height of Mount Everest (which is less than 9,000 meters high), and sufficient to raze the mightiest mountain range to sea level in a small fraction of geological time. In a few million years, with the mountains leveled, with the Earth's terrestrial regions reduced to flat featureless plains close to sea level, with the hydrological cycle no longer

FIGURE 2.1. NIAGARA FALLS

providing the vital twenty or so essential minerals from the rocks, terrestrial ecosystems would wither and die. So the hydrological cycle cannot perform its long-term task of leaching the elements of life from the rocks and nourishing terrestrial ecosystems without there being a continual input of new rock.

Oceanic life, no less than terrestrial, also needs continuous replenishment of the essential elements of life. We know from the fossil record that life has existed in the oceans for nearly four billion years (see comments on stromatolites in the next chapter), and this implies that the twenty-plus essential elements for life must have been present in the oceans throughout this immense period of time. The biological evidence for the chemical constancy of the world's oceans is even more compelling from the beginnings of the Cambrian era, 540 million years ago, to the present. The Cambrian strata contain fossil organisms closely related to many living animals, including snails, starfish, brachiopods (organisms similar in superficial appearance to bivalve mollusks and found throughout the seas today in intertidal zones), and arthropods such as trilobites (organisms resembling the familiar woodlouse). Even primitive fish (members of the same phylum to which all vertebrates belong, including ourselves) recently have been identified in Cambrian strata in China.[4] This zoo of diverse organisms could only have thrived in an ocean whose chemical and physical properties were practically identical to modern oceans. And since that ancient yesterday, the seas have been populated continuously with biota comparable in complexity to today's.

The chemical constancy is also evidenced by non-biological evidence. As geochemist Heinrich Holland comments, "The changes during the past 3.9 b.y. have not been dramatic... The mineralogy of marine evaporites indicates that the composition of seawater during the Phanerozoic cannot have varied greatly" in the past six hundred million years.[5] The composition has not of course remained *exactly constant*. There have been variations, for example, in the concentration of salt and in ocean acidity due to changes in atmospheric CO_2 levels.[6] But over long periods of time, as Michael Pilson comments, "the evidence from ancient salt deposits suggests a broad similarity in at least the major ion composition for at least the last 3500 million years."[7]

This constancy, stretching over billions of years, raises a paradox: The oceans have been continually losing the twenty or so vital essential elements over the entire time span in which marine life has existed, but the replacement supply could not come from land run-off due to erosion, because as mentioned above, the rate of land erosion would denude the continental crustal material completely in a few million years. Why do the oceans have so much nutrient mass to replace every year? Rachel Carson conveyed it in her inimitable style:

> When I think of the floor of the deep sea, the single, overwhelming fact that possesses my imagination is the accumulation of sediments. I see always the steady, unremitting, downward drift of materials from above, flake upon flake, layer upon layer—a drift that has continued for hundreds of millions of years... For the sediments are the materials of the most stupendous 'snowfall' the earth has ever seen.[8]

The vast chalk and limestone sediments ($CaCO_3$), in many places thousands of meters thick (the result of the raining down of the shells

FIGURE 2.2. WHITE CLIFFS OF DOVER

of microorganisms to the ocean floor over millions of years), are ample testimony to the massive loss of the elements in the oceans due to biogeochemical deposition and burial.

The current deposition rate of carbon into oceanic sediments is over twelve million metric tons per year, and the total carbon content of the oceans and atmosphere is over thirty-eight trillion metric tons. Yet despite the size of the carbon pool in the ocean and atmosphere, as the authors of *Elements of Physical Oceanography* point out, "Three million years will be sufficient to remove all the carbon... thus forcing the atmospheric PCO_2 to zero."[9] In effect, this would sterilize the oceans. Without CO_2, which is the carrier of the carbon atom to all life on Earth, there can be no carbon-based life in the oceans or on land. The various biogeochemical processes involved in the loss of minerals from the sea are complex, often involving the transit of a particular element through many organic and inorganic compounds before it is finally trapped in the accumulating sediments on the sea bed. Slow and complex, yes, but also inexorable. Without continual renewal of the mineral content of the oceans, the oceanic ecosystems would grind to a halt in a few million years and the Earth's oceans would become lifeless. Yes, the oceans receive nutrients from continental runoff, but there is not enough runoff, not enough continental landmass, to keep up with the rate of depletion.

And yet over many hundreds of millions of years, the oceans have not been rendered lifeless, nor the mountains ground into sterile plains. But how could there have been continents and mountains and life on land for 400 million years? And how could there have been life in the seas for four billion years? What mechanisms are continually remaking mountains and replenishing the mineral content of the ocean waters?

Plate Tectonics

UNTIL THE mid-twentieth century, no one had any clear idea how this replenishment occurred, where the input came from, or how the chemical constancy of the various components of the hydrosphere were maintained. Today the mystery has been essentially solved as a result of one of the more remarkable revolutions in scientific history, which arose from a number of key and unexpected discoveries between approximately 1955 and 1965. The "plate tectonic" revolution transformed the previous static conception of the world into one of a breathing, circulating, dynamic Earth, with continents moving across the globe on top of an underlying plastic mantle.[10] Before the 1960s, as Hazel Rhymer explained in *Nature*:

> The Earth was seen as a sphere with a thick, inert, rocky mantle encasing a central molten metallic core. The complex pattern of land and sea masses was believed to be essentially static. By the end of the [plate tectonic] revolution ten years later, only the core remained. The mantle had become a solid yet flowing region, convecting heat from within the Earth through a thin strong and brittle shell that was broken into a few large plates moving laterally on and with the mantle.[11]

Similarly, for Marcia Bjornerud, fellow of the Geological Society of America and Fulbright scholar, the plate tectonic revolution implied that

"Earth's surface and subsurface—like our own skin and organs—are in a constant state of renovation, the overall architecture preserved even as the constituent parts are incrementally replaced. Nothing is permanent, and yet *because* of this, everything is eternal."[12]

And it is because of tectonic recycling that each year the millions of tons of carbon, phosphorus, nitrogen, sulfur, and other essential elements of life sequestered in ocean sediments "are reincarnated again and again as minerals in rocks, gases in the atmosphere, ions in the ocean, schools of fishes, leaves on trees"; as Bjornerud explains, this planetary recycling job is "ubiquitous and obligatory… nothing is unusable waste."[13]

So plate tectonics explains why the continents exist and persist, why mountains are never finally ground to sea level, why the hydrological cycle can replenish the essential mineral content of the terrestrial hydrosphere endlessly over billions of years, ensuring the continuance of life on land, and why the seas have never been depleted of their dissolved salt and mineral content. Plate tectonics has revealed that as fast as the hydrological cycle is wearing down the rocks, and as fast as the ocean sediments are entombing life's essential elements on the sea bed, tectonic processes have been continually replacing them.

Plate tectonics created the Himalayas, and while the Indus river is busy wearing away the western Himalayas, tectonic uplift at a rate of ten millimeters per year[14] is continually renewing them. It is because of tectonic uplift that the hydrological cycle has been able to continuously deliver the core mineral constituents of life to terrestrial ecosystems over the past 400 million years.

As knowledge of plate tectonics has grown over the past half century, it has become increasingly apparent that water plays a crucial role in lubricating the entire tectonic system. Indeed, without its lubricating action, the movement of the great plates would have long ago ground to a halt. Earth is the only planet in the inner solar system with oceans and vast quantities of water, and this is a prime reason for Earth's highly active tectonic system. Among the planets of our solar system, as Marcia Bjornerud points out, "Only Earth developed habits of self-maintenance

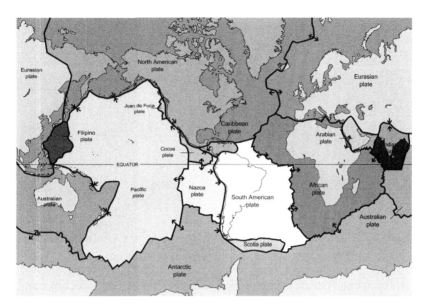

FIGURE 2.3. THE TECTONIC PLATES. ARROWS DENOTE DIRECTION OF MOTION OF PLATES. SOME ARE CONVERGING AND OTHERS DIVERGING.

that have kept it looking youthful and fresh," and as she continues: "Earth's beauty secret: Water, and lots of it."[15]

The Tectonic Plates

ALTHOUGH a detailed description of plate tectonics is beyond the scope of this chapter, a brief outline is in order so that the central role water plays in the process can be understood.[16]

According to the plate tectonic model of Earth, the rocky and solid upper layer of planet Earth, the lithosphere, consists of several distinct tectonic plates. These sit on a hot upper mantle, known as the asthenosphere.[17] The plates are driven across the Earth's surface by movements in the underlying viscous upper mantle. Think of sheets of polar ice floating on the warmer water beneath and in perpetual motion driven by the ocean currents in the underlying water.

There are two types of tectonic plates—oceanic and continental. The continental plates can be up to 250 kilometers thick. The oceanic plates are denser but thinner—only 100–150 kilometers thick when mature.[18]

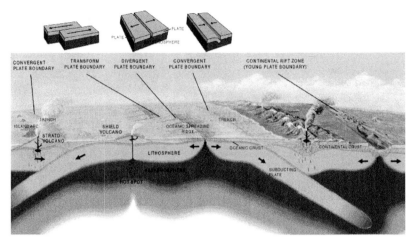

FIGURE 2.4. DIVERGENT AND CONVERGENT PLATE BOUNDARIES.

The upper layer of each type of plate is termed the crust (the oceanic and continental crust, respectively). Oceanic crust is relatively thin (about six to seven kilometers) compared with continental crust (thirty-five to forty-five kilometers). Plate movement ranges from a few millimeters to about fifteen centimeters per year.

Plates are being continually created at "divergent or constructive plate boundaries" where hot magma rises from the mantle to the surface, solidifies, and moves laterally away from the boundary, initiating the creation of two new plates (see Figure 2.4).

Because oceanic plates are formed at constructive boundaries under the sea (such as those which exist today in the Atlantic or Pacific mid-ocean ridges), sea water penetrates the hot congealing magma down to a depth of seven kilometers, interacting with it to form new oceanic crust that sits atop the nascent plate. As the nascent plate (consisting at first mainly of oceanic crust) moves away from the divergent boundary it cools, and material drawn from the underlying viscous mantle accretes to its base. This process, operating over millions of years, eventually creates a mature, solid, and rigid oceanic lithospheric plate consisting of a crust approximately seven kilometers thick overlying approximately 100 kilometers of rigid material accreted from the more viscous upper mantle rocks.

FIGURE 2.5. RIFT CAUSED BY DIVERGENT BOUNDARY IN ICELAND IN THINGVELLIR NATIONAL PARK.

Every newly created oceanic plate is destined to return to the mantle at a so-called "convergent boundary" or subduction zone, where two plates collide and where one, the heavier plate with its load of crustal material, sinks back into the mantle from which it emerged millions of years earlier—until it is reborn at another mid-ocean ridge when the whole cycle is repeated (see Figure 2.4). Initially, the new hot oceanic plate close to a divergent boundary is less dense than the underlying mantle rocks on which it sits. But as it moves away from the divergent boundary at which it was formed, it becomes denser with age as it cools and thickens, allowing the plate to subduct back into the mantle at subduction zones.

Where a divergent boundary occurs in the middle of a continental landmass, as the nascent plates diverge they pull the earth apart creating valleys, trenches, and gorges, such as the Great Rift Valley in Africa or the gorges in the Thingvellir National Park in Iceland (see Figure 2.5).

When a heavy oceanic plate with its dense oceanic crust meets (converges) with a lighter continental plate with its less dense continental crust, the heavier oceanic plate and its crust subducts or sinks back into the mantle (see Figure 2.4 above). This is occurring today as the Nazca plate subducts under the South American plate at the western edge of South America. The forces released as the plates collide cause uplifting and crumpling of the continental crust atop the South American plate, forming the Andes mountain chain.[19] Another outcome of the subduction of the oceanic plate (discussed further below) is the release of water and ions from the subducting plate and its overlying oceanic crust, generating new molten continental granitic crust in the wedge of mantle above the subducting plate (see Figure 2.4). The subducting plate fuses with the existing continental crust, and in places it rises to the surface to be extruded via volcanic activity.

Where two plates carrying continental crust collide, as with the Indian and Eurasian plates, one (the Indian plate) subducts under the other (the Eurasian plate). The latter is uplifted, and the result in this case is the Himalayas.

In some places, plates slide past each other and neither subducts, as occurs along the San Andreas Fault in California, which forms the boundary between the North American Plate and the Pacific Plate (see Figure 2.4).

In passing, it is worth noting that though Alfred Wegener first proposed the theory of continental drift in 1912, the geological establishment rejected it for decades, clinging to the outmoded theory of immobile continents.[20] This, and the triumph of Wegener's theory after the discovery of abundant evidence for continental drift, is one of the most dramatic examples of a scientific revolution in history.[21]

The Dynamic Mantle

It is widely acknowledged that movements in the mantle rocks that underlie the tectonic plates are largely responsible for moving the plates, even though the relative importance of the various mechanisms involved are not fully understood. But it is clear that the mantle rocks must be able to move if motion is to be imparted to the tectonic plates. And it is clear that mantle movement and convectional currents are in turn only possible because a host of conditions are just right. As Bjornerud points out:

> If rocks were better conductors of heat, such stirring would never take place, because the necessary temperature contrasts would be subdued. If rocks didn't expand significantly when heated, there would be no density instability to drive convection. If the viscosity of Earth's mantle rocks were much higher, the whole system would grind to a halt. Finally, if the planet had a smaller inventory of radioactive elements [an inventory which was largely determined by the cosmic abundance of the elements], or if these had much shorter half lives, the bulb in the planetary lava lamp would have burned out long ago. But Earth's mantle keeps on turning.[22]

But of all the factors which must be right for the mantle rocks to be mobilized, one of the most critical is viscosity. And one of the most important determinants of mantle viscosity is water.[23] For instance, olivine is one common mineral in the mantle, and when it is free of water it is very strong. But as one standard textbook explains, olivine "is capable of dissolving small but significant quantities of H_2O,"[24] which modifies olivine's internal structure and reduces its strength. As the authors point out, dry olivine is 100 times stronger than wet olivine, and "The amount of H_2O required to reduce the strength of olivine significantly is surprisingly small, of the order of 50 ppm."[25] This is, as they point out, two to ten times less than the water content of the mantle. The authors continue:

FIGURE 2.6. LAVA SPOUTING IN HAWAII.

This has clear implication for the way the mantle behaves under stress because olivine comprises 50–60 % of the upper mantle. For example, the strength of olivine determines how the mantle responds to isostatic loading by the overlying crust and lithosphere. Clearly a weaker mantle will respond more rapidly to isostatic loading or unloading than a strong mantle. Weakening olivine allows the mantle to undergo solid-state flow more easily, and so aids mantle flow. To put it another way, water alters the dynamic viscosity of the mantle.... the overall effect of more than 50 ppm water in olivine is to reduce the dynamic viscosity of the mantle by two to three orders of magnitude (by a factor of 100–1000).

This is, as they show, just right to allow mantle convection and hence plate tectonics. Summarizing, they comment, "The H_2O content of the mantle has a controlling effect on both the style and vigour of mantle convection and the development of lithospheric plates, even at the small concentrations present in the mantle today."[26]

But water has another transformative influence on the mantle rocks: It greatly lowers the temperature at which melting can occur in the mantle[27] by up to 800°C.[28] How does water do it? Eric Klemetti, professor of geosciences at Denison University, explains:

> Add water into a mantle peridotite and it will melt at a lower temperature because the bonds in the minerals that make up the rock will be disrupted by the water molecule (we call it a "network modifier"). In a subduction zone (like the Cascades or the Andes), where an oceanic plate slides down under another plate, that down going slab releases its water as it heats up. That water then rises up into the mantle above it, causing it to melt at a lower temperature.[29]

Thus, water not only enables the mantle to move, but also enables melting to occur. Without the mobility of the mantle, the plates would be immobile. Without melting, there would be no molten magma to rise to the surface to generate the nascent continental crust in the wedge above a subducting plate, and no magma rising to the surface at divergent boundaries to initiate the formation of new oceanic crust and oceanic plates. Indeed, there would be no plates, and no plate tectonics.

In inducing melting and reducing the viscosity of the mantle, water enables a chain reaction that generates the whole plate tectonic system, which leads to the replenishing of the vital minerals of life in both oceanic and terrestrial hydrospheres, and both forms and recycles the continental crust, a crucial condition for terrestrial life.

It is fortunate indeed that the Earth possesses vast amounts of water. Without it, through the eons of geological time, the mantle would neither have moved nor melted, and the tectonic wheels would never have turned; there would be no recycling of either the oceanic or continental crust. But just how does the mantle acquire its vital supply of water? The delivery turns out to be via a second important component of the tectonic system—oceanic crust recycling.

Recycling of the Oceanic Crust

As THE upwelling magma cools and meets the sea at the mid-ocean ridges, its various mineral constituents interact with sea water and are altered in various ways to form nascent hydrated oceanic crust. These interactions are aided by the high porosity and permeability of the newly congealing magma as it cools and interacts with the sea water. As Jonathan Lunine comments:

> The basalt at the mid-ocean ridges solidifies as it approaches the surface. Because the ridges are underwater, the basalts react with the water, which becomes incorporated in the crystal structure of the rocks, *hydrating* the minerals. The process can be very efficient because the mid-ocean ridges are filled with cracks, through which water circulates in an intricate network of hydrothermal systems. Much like the cells in our body receive nourishment through an intricate network of capillaries, oceanic basalts enjoy extensive and intimate contact with water."[30] [emphasis in original]

Altogether, newly formed hydrated ocean crust (the upper seven kilometers of the infant plate) can contain as much as five percent or more of water.[31] Frisch et al. (2011) describe the reaction between sea water and magma. Ocean water "percolates through fractures and joints of the ocean crust down to depths of several kilometres," they write. "During this process water is heated… and causes substantial modifications to magmatic rocks." These changes involve "the process of OH^- (hydroxyl) ions binding to minerals and thus transforming the 'dry' magmatic minerals into 'wet' metamorphic ones."[32]

Then, even millions of years after it was first formed, the now old cold and dense crust still retains considerable water as it subducts into the mantle at a subduction zone.[33] And as we've seen, as the plate with its hydrated crust descends (see Figure 2.4), the pressure and heat dehydrate the minerals and water is released into the mantle. The amount of water returned to the mantle in this way is considerable. As the author of a post from the *Earth–Pages* website points out, in a million years up to 318 billion tons of water are returned to the mantle. In eighty million years, the entire volume of the world's oceans is recycled.[34]

The significance of the delivery of such a vast quantity of water to the mantle can hardly be exaggerated. For it is this delivery via the recycling of hydrated minerals generated at the mid-ocean ridges that animates the mantle and confers upon it the crucial properties required to drive the tectonic system.

So just as water delivers itself by its own properties to the thirsty land via the hydrological system, water by its own powers delivers itself to the mantle, and thereby activates the whole tectonic system, and sustains it over long ages. The authors of *An Introduction to Our Dynamic Planet* stress, "The only way in which that H_2O content [of the mantle] can be maintained over geological time is as a result of recycling of water from the oceans through hydrothermal modification of the ocean crust and subduction of the resultant hydrated minerals."[35] Thus does water, by her own powers, animate the mantle rocks, bringing them to life and initiating plate tectonics. Through one of the ends of the tectonic system— oceanic crust recycling—water delivers herself to the mantle to ensure that the tectonic system can continue working for billions of years.

Without the unique fitness of water to hydrate the magma at the mid-ocean ridges, there is no way that water could be carried in such quantities into the mantle from the ocean. And without water the tectonic system would grind to a halt, and oceanic and continental recycling would cease (see below). This process has several other important consequences as well, which will be discussed in detail in the next chapter.

Replenishing the Seas

NATURE—WITH ITS genius for parsimony—has another use for the fateful meeting of water and magma, one mentioned earlier in this chapter but that deserves further consideration.

There has always been evidence that the mineral content of sea water cannot be accounted for entirely by continental runoff. If the ocean's waters are merely concentrated stream and river water, then the "elements should be present in the same ratios in both types of water," *The Water Encyclopedia* notes, however, that "the ratio patterns for most components for the two water types are quite different. This pattern means that simple evaporation of water cannot change river water into sea water."[36]

The proportions of salts in isolated, salty inland lakes, such as Utah's Great Salt Lake or the Dead Sea, are much different from the proportions of salts in the ocean, so weathering and erosion of continental crustal rocks cannot be the only source of sea salts. River water is generally a dilute solution of bicarbonate and calcium ions, while the principal ions in seawater are chloride and sodium. Again, the magnesium content of seawater should be higher if seawater were simply concentrated river water.[37]

The difference is explained by the meeting of sea water and magma, which changes the composition of sea water compared to river water. As the authors of *An Introduction to Our Dynamic Planet* comment:

> Because normal seawater enters the hydrothermal system but hot, mineral-rich water exits the system, the overall process results in a change to the original composition of the crust. Equally, the input of hydrothermal fluid… adds components to sea water. Through these effects… the oceanic crust becomes depleted in some elements (particularly Mg) and enriched in others (such as Mn and Fe).[38]

The fact that the upper mantle appears to contain more (and similar proportions) of the substances found in sea water (including the water itself) than are found in surface rocks further highlights the important contribution that the mid-ocean ridge ionic exchange makes to the composition of sea water.[39]

Oceanic plate and crust recycling, by cycling the Earth's water through the mantle, is not only essential to maintaining the mobility of the mantle and its ability to turn the tectonic wheels—including oceanic recycling itself—but also provides a mechanism for maintaining the constancy of the chemical composition of the oceans. This is essential if life is to persist in the sea.

As well as the interactions between sea water and nascent crust at mid-ocean ridges and continental run-off, another tectonic process that influences the salt level in the oceans is the formation of evaporites. These form in marine basins in which the flow of seawater into the basin is not balanced by outflow, where most of the water lost from the basin

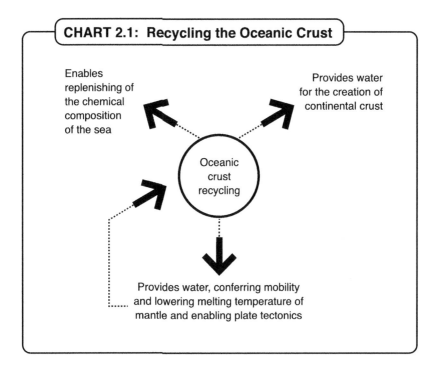

CHART 2.1: Recycling the Oceanic Crust

Enables replenishing of the chemical composition of the sea

Provides water for the creation of continental crust

Oceanic crust recycling

Provides water, conferring mobility and lowering melting temperature of mantle and enabling plate tectonics

is via evaporation, resulting in the precipitation and deposition of vast salt deposits and their subsequent uplift at convergent boundaries. As L. Paul Knauth argues, the salinity of the ocean would be as much as "1.6–2x the modern value or even higher, if all the salt and brine currently sequestered on the continents were returned to the ocean from which it was extracted by sedimentation on continents."[40] Moreover, Knauth speculates that the lowering of oceanic salinity caused by the laying down of vast beds of salt in late pre-Cambrian times may have played a role in the subsequent emergence of complex metazoan life, as it would have inevitably increased the solubility and availability of oxygen in the oceans.

Recycling the Continental Crust

OCEANIC RECYCLING has yet another important role to play—one also touched on briefly early in this chapter: The water drawn down into the subduction zone plays a unique and critical role in forming continental crust and continents, a prerequisite for terrestrial life. As the authors of *Introduction to our Dynamic Planet* comment:

> The continents literally form the bedrock of our existence; they are the source of all our raw materials and provide a platform above the surface of the oceans on which terrestrial life has evolved.... As Bill Bryson puts it in his book *A Short History of Nearly Everything* (2003), without the continents "There might be life in that lonesome ocean, but there certainly wouldn't be football." More significantly, however, the continents define the inorganic chemical environment within which all life has evolved, even marine life, because critical aspects of ocean chemistry are controlled by continental run-off.[41]

We saw in Chapter 1 that water is uniquely suited to support land-based life in that, through its own talents, it delivers itself to terrestrial ecosystems with its precious cargo of mineral nutrients. Remarkably, water is also involved in forming the very mountains which it erodes and weathers to such life-giving effect. Water is a crucial ingredient in the mix of molten rock that congeals to form continental crust, and is also directly involved in enabling the tectonic cycling system, which in turn enables the reaction chamber where the first fateful steps to continental crust are forged.[42] Thus, water is fit to make mountains and fit to erode them, providing the terrestrial hydrosphere (and land-based life) with essential nutrients. As always, we are indebted to water's creative magic more than we might ever have suspected.

The details of the various chemical reactions and geophysical processes that lead to the production of granitic rocks are complex and beyond the scope of this chapter. Briefly, though, as mentioned above, when an oceanic plate dips down into the mantle (a process happening today as the Nazca plate subducts under the South American), the increasing heat and pressure squeezes out more water and ions from the sinking oceanic crust into the overlying wedge of mantle material (see Figure 2.4). This extrusion of water has a profound effect on the properties of the wedge of mantle rock above the subducting oceanic crust, causing it to melt. This initiates a series of chemical and physical processes that ultimately result in the production of the granitic rock characteristic of continental crust, what Bjornerud calls in *Reading the Rocks*, "the buoyant granitic distillate unique to earth."[43]

Not all the details of the mechanisms involved in the manufacture of granitic continental crust are fully understood. Jonathan Lunine refers to it as a "puzzle,"[44] but it is universally acknowledged that water plays a critical role.[45] Indeed the authors of a classic 1983 paper in the field, I. H. Campbell and S. R. Taylor, entitled it "No water, no granites — no oceans, no continents."[46] A more recent paper explains:

> Campbell and Taylor (1983) emphasized the 'essential role of water in the formation of granites' and, in turn, continents and introduced to the literature the important concept of 'no water, no granites, no oceans, no continents'. They argued that the Earth, which is the only inner planet with abundant water, is the only planet with granite and continents, whereas the Moon and the other inner planets have little or no water and no granites or continents. This concept could be extended to: 'no water, no plate tectonics, no continents', since with no water plate tectonics is unlikely to work. Thus, there is a fundamental linkage between formation of granitic (granodioritic) continental crust and plate-tectonic mechanism.[47]

The newly-melted molten mantle material, chemically cooked and changed by reaction with water and ions in the mantle wedge, is lighter than the mantle rocks from which it is distilled, so it rises because of its buoyancy. It eventually cools and congeals into new continental crust, ensuring that there will be continents and land on Earth where terrestrial life can thrive.

But why, if the granitic distillate is so light, is Mount Everest only 8,800 meters high? Why have mountains not grown continually like Mount Olympus on Mars, which is nearly twenty-two kilometers high—nearly two and a half times the height of Mount Everest? Marcia Bjornerud asked the same question. As she points out, "[if] it is not possible to subduct continental crust—the Himalaya Mountains illustrate the stubborn refusal of buoyant continental crust to be pushed down into the mantle—why hasn't the volume of continental crust been growing steadily through time? How has Earth been getting rid of the stuff? The answer is… raindrops."[48] [ellipsis in original]

Water again to the rescue! Or more specifically, the hydrological cycle, which grinds down the continental crust and delivers it to the sea bed for subduction into the mantle and eventual recycling.

But how exactly do the insoluble sediments—particles of rock—derived from erosion of continental crust, return to the mantle for recycling? The only way to take continentally-derived sediments back to the mantle is to take it so far out to sea that it gets a ride on what Bjornerud calls: "the oceanic express and goes down with [the oceanic crust as a] a subducting slab."[49] Some of the great river systems do indeed deposit their sediments hundreds of miles out beyond the continental shelf on the deep sea floor—right on top of the oceanic express![50]

So water again comes to the rescue, carrying the detritus far out to sea. Earthquakes also shake sediments on to the deep sea floor for subduction on the same "oceanic express."[51] So the sedimentary detritus from the great mountain ranges caused by water erosion is carried by water onto the abyssal plain beyond the continental shelf. From there it eventually returns to the mantle, pulled down on top of the subducting oceanic crust where it combines with water (released from the sinking oceanic crust) and mantle material in the wedge above the subduction slab, regenerating continental crust, and the great mountain ranges. Ultimately, through erosion by water, the familiar topography and land forms of the Earth are created.

This provides another glimpse of the profound fitness in the properties of water for life on land. For if not for the properties of water, there would be no light granitic or felsic continental crust, no continents, and no environment on Earth for terrestrial organisms. And if it were not for another set of unique properties of water (discussed in the previous chapter), neither would there be any hydrological cycle supplying land-based life with water and its life-giving cargo of dissolved minerals. Water is thus critically involved in generating two fundamental and necessary conditions for land-based life. Water is not only involved in making the continents but also in delivering, by its own powers, itself and its vital cargo of essential minerals to land-based life forms.

Paradox Resolved: We opened this chapter with a paradox: The mineral constancy of the terrestrial and oceanic hydrosphere is maintained over immense periods of time in the face of continual erosion of continental crust and deposition of minerals from the oceans into sediments on the sea bed. The resolution of the paradox is now apparent: The tectonic recycling of the oceanic and continental crusts holds the key. Because of tectonic recycling, the continental crust is being continually formed and uplifted. This means that the erosion of the mountains can continue to supply the terrestrial hydrosphere with necessary minerals without cessation, as long as Earth exists and has an ocean. And despite the rate of erosion of the mountains, runoff from the land can fertilize the sea waters, not for a limited period of a few million years but *for billions of years*. And the continual recycling of the oceanic crust, as the sea water interacts with the hot upwelling magma, provides a second ongoing and endless means of mineral input to replenish oceanic waters.[52] So, balanced against the continual and massive loss of minerals to the sea bed, tectonic recycling replenishes the oceans with continental runoff and by the reaction of water with upwelling magma at the mid-ocean ridges.

This means that the constancy of the elemental composition of both the terrestrial waters and the oceans is ultimately due to the properties of water. Water, by her own properties, through the weathering of the rocks and through the interaction with nascent oceanic crust, ensures that the chemical composition of the terrestrial and oceanic hydrosphere will be maintained.

Gratuity

WE SAW in the previous chapter that water's own specific forms (from a stormy sea to a calving glacier) are amazingly diverse, but the landforms created as the end result of water's role in tectonic recycling of continental crust are even more spectacular. Philip Ball reminds us:

FIGURE 2.7. TORRES DEL PAINE NATIONAL PARK

For all its fluidity, water is also one of the main shaping agents of nature. It makes rugged corrugations in highlands, carving out the intaglio of river valleys. It eats away at coastlines to generate underhangs and caves and eventually to collapse them, and to shift entire beaches down the coast. On its course from mountain to sea it may leave exquisite rock sculptures in its path. Cycles of freezing and thawing split apart the firmest of rocks, reducing slopes to rubble... And in tongues of ice, water scours the Earth into broad valleys and shifts huge boulders over great distances.[53]

It is water (as liquid and as ice) that has shaped the sawtooth mountains of Patagonia, the ice-sculpted U-shaped valleys of Yosemite and the Alps, the flat flood plains of the Amazon, and great cataracts such as Niagara. The erosional effects of water have played a paramount role in all such landforms. Without this erosional work the topography of the land would be boringly smooth and gradual; there would be no river valleys, no jagged sawtooth mountains, no Grand Tetons, no Himalayas. The magnificent beaches, cliffs, and sand dunes at the coastal interface of land and sea throughout the world are also due to the erosional work of sea water. And of course, without water we would not be here to witness such an impoverished landscape, because the work of water that generates this magnificent panorama is the end of the tectonic wheel and the great hydrological cycle, without which terrestrial life would be impossible.

It is gratuitous indeed, that while water is busy playing its diverse roles in recycling the rocks, delivering life's matrix to land-based ecosystems, and enriching the global hydrosphere, it is also creating such magnificence.

Summary

FROM THE evidence reviewed in this chapter, water's role is indeed, as Bjornerud comments, "profound" and "surprising."[54] As she comments, "All parts of the fabrication and recycling process are cleverly linked and powered largely by water," she writes. "The destruction of ocean crust via subduction leads to the formation of continental crust through *water*-facilitated melting. The destruction of continental crust via water-driven erosion ultimately replenishes the mantle for the next round of… crust production." She concludes with language whose teleological implications are hard to ignore: "Efficient, sustainable, robust, and elegant, the system would win top honors in an industrial design competition."[55]

The three core tectonic processes described above—the forming and recycling of oceanic crust, the recycling of continental crust, and mantle movement (which is the ultimate engine of the whole integrated system)—all critically depend on the physical and chemical properties of water. As far as we know, there is no other fluid which could substitute for water in these three processes. If water did not have exactly the properties it has, there would be no plate tectonics and all the basic biogeochemical cycles that allow life on Earth would grind to a halt. To paraphrase Voltaire, "If water did not exist it would have to be invented."[56]

The teleological wonder of plate tectonics is not that each component wheel depends on the properties of water—that is wonder enough—but that each wheel depends on the turning of the others, and each depends on water, so that the entire integrated system depends on water as lubricant. And it is only because water has greased all the component wheels and enabled their turning in perfect unison for billions of years that there is life in the seas or on the land.

We saw in the previous chapter that water's existence in three material states on Earth is logically and causally prior to the exploitation of water's several unique erosional properties for life on land, which together can be seen to make up a teleological hierarchy of interacting properties. This chapter has shown that the life-giving properties of the hydrological cycle are themselves possible only because of a necessary prior fitness in nature for tectonic recycling. Moreover, this prior fitness depends in large part on the properties of water. Thus the properties of water make possible the hydrological system, and by enabling the tectonic wheels to turn create the very continents upon which the vital rain falls. It is surely a wonder that the fluid so fit to form the matrix of carbon-based cellular life (Chapter 7) and for mammalian physiology (Chapter 6) should also be fit to create the necessary global environmental conditions that carbon-based life forms need to thrive.

An intriguing aspect of the causal sequence exhibited in the tectonic system is that the subsystems that keep the whole causal chain moving are reciprocally self-formative. Consider mantle melting and mobility (enabled by water): this causes oceanic crust to form at mid-ocean ridges, and then later to be recycled via subduction back into the mantle. But oceanic crust recycling (by delivering water to the mantle) also causes mantle movement and melting. Again, the upwelling of the magma at the mid-ocean ridges is the cause of two ends (oceanic crust and continental crust). The former, in turn is a cause of the latter, through subduction and melting to produce granite rock (which makes up a large portion of continental crust). But because the ends (oceanic crust and continental crust) are returned to the mantle (by subduction and erosion) from which they originated, they are both also causes of the mantle itself (see Figure 2.8).

The design of such systems, in which the parts are reciprocally self-formative, transcends the design of any artifact or machine ever created.

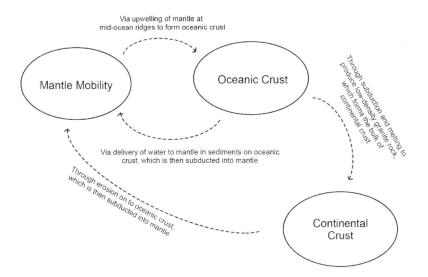

FIGURE 2.8.

The parts of a jumbo jet or computer are not reciprocally self-formative; they play no part in the formation of other parts of the whole or system. They may function together to serve the whole but are not a cause of the other parts of the whole. The engine of a jumbo jet plays no part in the manufacture of the wings.

It is interesting to recall that Kant (1790), in a well-known section of his *Critique of Judgement*,[57] argues that a defining characteristic of a living system (what he calls a "natural purpose ") is the formative reciprocity of their parts. He points out that systems, more specifically living organisms, whose parts exhibit such a reciprocal formative influence on each other, belong to a completely different order of being than that of contingent artifactual assemblages. For example, in the case of a watch (or a jumbo jet), although it is true that each part is there for the sake of the others so that they might coherently function together for a purpose (telling the time or flying), the parts do not owe their presence to the agency of the others. In Kant's words, "Hence a watch wheel does not produce other wheels, still less does one watch produce other watches… An organized [natural] being is then not a mere machine," for it "possesses in itself *formative* power of a self-propagating kind."[58] [emphasis in original] And Kant insists, "This can never be the case with artificial instruments."[59] Natural purposes exhibit "nothing analogous to any causality we know."[60] He defines a natural whole or system as "an organized product of nature… in which every part is reciprocally purpose (end) and means."[61]

Not one artifact produced to date, including the most complex advanced robots and intelligent machines, is composed of parts which are agents in the generation of other parts of the same artifact. Only in the field of artificial life is it possible to conceive of an artificially fabricated biochemical doppelganger of the canonical cell that would challenge Kant's claim—an artifact in which the parts exhibit genuine reciprocal formative powers. But even in this field, a genuinely novel living cell, composed of parts that exhibit formative reciprocity, has still not been achieved. (Although the Earth's dynamic system far exceeds that of a watch or jumbo jet in terms of its reciprocal, formative powers, the Earth does not of course produce copies of itself, so it doesn't meet every aspect of Kant's definition of a living system.)

The tectonic system is not only, as described by Bjornerud, "efficient, sustainable, robust, and elegant"[62]; in its self-formative ability, it transcends any design in the domain of the artifact.

The notion that the tectonic system is the result of design rises unbidden from the evidence. How could such an elegant system of integrated elements of unique fitness, which has fashioned the world for life over billions of years, and which transcends in its reciprocal self-formative abilities any artifact created to date, have arisen out of blind collisions of atoms? And how could the manifold fitness of water, which conveys every impression of having been fine-tuned to turn the wheels, be mere happenstance?

And, as we will see, there is more evidence of a special fitness in nature for life on land—a suggestion wonderfully confirmed by material explored in the following chapters.

3. PRESERVING THE OCEAN

It's easy to forget that the story of Earth's water, from gentle rains to raging rivers, is intimately connected to the larger story of our solar system and beyond. But our water came from somewhere—every world in our solar system got its water from the same shared source. So it's worth considering that the next glass of water you drink could easily have been part of a comet, or an ocean moon, or a long-vanished sea on the surface of Mars. And note that the night sky may be full of exoplanets formed by similar processes to our home world, where gentle waves wash against the shores of alien seas.

From NASA article: "The Solar System and Beyond is Awash with Water" (2015)[1]

Twenty-six years ago when I first started writing this book, I had no clear idea of what Gaia was although I had thought deeply about her. What I did know was that the Earth was very different from Mars and Venus. It was a planet with apparently the strange property of keeping itself always a fit and comfortable place for living things to inhabit.

James Lovelock, *Gaia* (2001)[2]

STANDING IN THE INTERTIDAL ZONE ALONG THE SHORE OF HAMElin Pool, a saline lagoon in Shark Bay, West Australia, are hundreds of curious columnar, rock-like formations rising in some cases to about a meter in height. These are stromatolites, layered or banded formations built up over three to four thousand years by the actions of bacterial biofilms, composed of primitive cyanobacteria or blue-green algae. The growth of successive layers of bacteria one on top of the other produces a typical banded pattern and a basic columnar shape.

Not far from Shark Bay, over vast areas of West Australia, are extensive fossilized formations exhibiting the typical laminations of modern stromatolites. Though very similar to those in Shark Bay, they are dated to an era in the remote past, 2.7 billion years ago.[3] And an even more

FIGURE 3.1. THE OLDEST LIVING FOSSILS. STROMATOLITES IN HAMELIN POOL NATURE RESERVE, SHARK BAY, WEST AUSTRALIA.

ancient banded formation, also situated in West Australia, has been dated at 3.4 billion years old.[4] According to a very recent report, some Greenland stromatolite fossils are even older, dated at 3.7–3.8 billion years.[5] These findings make these stromatolites by far the oldest fossils on Earth yet discovered. Gazing on the product of life forms that thrived in the world ocean nearly four billion years ago—a time span beyond ordinary human comprehension—is a truly humbling experience.

The continuous thriving of marine life forms (such as the stromatolites) over such a vast period of time implies that the chemical composition of the oceans must have contained all the elements necessary for life throughout that time—a massive testimony to the efficiency of the tectonic recycling of the Earth's crustal materials.

But it also means that the oceans themselves must have existed through the entire span of geological time and that the temperature of the atmosphere and hydrosphere must have remained close to ambient temperatures.

As James Lovelock (ex-NASA atmospheric consultant) points out, the continuous existence of the ocean since the formation of the Earth is also documented by the great beds of marine sediments found throughout the geological record.[6] Moreover, there is also evidence suggesting that the volume of the oceans has remained relatively constant.[7]

The oceans are causally prior to almost everything else on Earth. Before there can be tectonic recycling and all that follows, *there must be an ocean*. Before there can be continental crust, *there must be an ocean*. Before tectonic recycling can refresh the mineral content of the oceans, before there can be a hydrological cycle and erosion of the rocks to fertilize the land, *there must be an ocean*. Before there can be soil and plants on land, *there must be an ocean*. Before the evolution of life can take place over billions of years, *there must be an ocean*. Before there can be a world remotely resembling our home, *there must be an ocean*.

What factors have preserved the world's ocean and the Earth's temperature—two strands of what are an inseparable braid—in the ambient range over time-spans beyond any ordinary human understanding? What factors have preserved such clement conditions on Earth for four billion years? As Marcia Bjornerud concedes in her *Reading the Rocks*, "We don't entirely know. But if this equilibrium had not prevailed, we would never have emerged to wonder about such things. Sentient life could only have emerged on a planet that has provided consistently and benevolently for its denizens."[8]

Lovelock was so impressed by the extraordinary stability and clemency of the Earth's environment and hydrosphere, that he speculated that the Earth might be a self-regulating "super-organism" which he designated *Gaia*, after the Earth-goddess of the Greeks.[9] The fact that a world authority on climatology and atmospheric science should find the environmental constancy so extraordinary that he felt moved to propose such an exotic explanation is testimony to just how extraordinary Earth's interdependent system of self-regulation really is.

Here in this chapter we will see that the conservation of water as a liquid on Earth and the maintenance of the Earth's hydrosphere in the ambient temperature range through billions of years is the result of a combination of unique properties of water, which again, as it were, conspire together to achieve Lovelock's "miracle of *Gaia*." And it is not just the preservation of the oceans and global temperature that has been largely the work of water. Water was also involved in the first step towards the formation of the Earth: the formation of planetesimals from cosmic dust which then accreted to form ever larger clumps of matter, leading eventually to the formation of the protoplanetary disk, the planetary system, and our planet's oceans.

Creator of Worlds

BEFORE THERE can be oceans, there must be planetary homes like the Earth on which to house them. The role of water in the formation of the solar system and the Earth was alluded to by Ewine van Dishoeck of Leiden Observatory in a recent paper for *Europhysics*: "Water is a key molecule in the cosmos, from distant galaxies and star-forming regions in the Milky Way to the Solar System and our own blue planet," and not merely present but an active agent involved in key "episodes in the process of stellar birth" and the formation of planets.[10]

Water assists in the birth of planets in two ways. As van Dishoeck comments in another paper, "Water in gaseous form acts as a coolant that allows interstellar gas clouds to collapse to form stars, whereas water ice facilitates the sticking of small dust particles that eventually must grow to planetesimals and planets."[11]

The importance of water in initiating the formation of dust particles and their accretion into planetesimals is highlighted in another recent article:

> Water ice is one of the most abundant materials in dense molecular clouds and in the outer reaches of protoplanetary disks. In contrast to other materials (e.g., silicates), water ice is assumed to be stickier due to its higher specific surface energy, leading to faster or more efficient growth in mutual collisions... Our experimental results indicate that the presence of water ice in the outer reaches of proto-

FIGURE 3.2. STELLAR NURSERY IN THE LARGE MAGELLANIC CLOUD.

planetary disks can enhance the growth of planetesimals by direct sticking of particles.[12]

"Star formation: it's what every world needs," Philip Ball writes. "To make a planet, you first have to make a sun."[13] And to make stars in star-forming galactic nurseries enriched with metal atoms—like the region our own solar system was formed in and in which habitable planetary systems are born—water helps cool the nebulae,[14] promoting their collapse and the formation of solar systems and planets.

It's true that in galactic star nurseries in metal-poor regions of a galaxy, water has a very low abundance and is not a factor in star formation. But to make a star capable of hosting a habitable planetary system such as ours,[15] you need water, and to have life originate and evolve and thrive on such a terrestrial planet you need water. Indeed, to turn the great geophysical wheels, you need water in vast quantities. You need an ocean!

FIGURE 3.3. THE BLUE PLANET. TAKEN FROM APOLLO 17

Creator of Oceans

AND HOW did we get our ocean? It turns out that water was not just involved in the first creative steps on the path to the Solar System, the Sun, and planet Earth. The properties of water were also critically involved in the very formation of the oceans, and not just in their role of filling the ocean basins. We saw in Chapter 1 that the delivery of water to the terrestrial areas of Earth for organisms like ourselves depends entirely on the unique fitness of water to this end—that it exists in three material states, solid, liquid, and gas in ambient conditions, and that the delivery of water to the land depends on the properties of water itself. As we will now see again, it was the unique physical and chemical properties of water itself that played a critical role in the origins of the oceans shortly after the formation of the Earth.

Although exactly how Earth obtained her water and became a blue planet is still controversial, both of the two proposed mechanisms depend on the unique intrinsic properties of water itself.

According to the most popular model, which might be termed "the amphibolic model," no free water survived the initial formation of the planets in the inner regions of the Solar System, scorched as they were by the young hot Sun. But water was conserved in what Bjornerud calls "a heat-proof vault"[16] in hydrous silicate minerals, like olivine, which make up (as we saw in the previous chapter) a considerable proportion of the mantle of the Earth. These were able to hold on to their water despite the hothouse atmosphere in the young inner solar system. (In many silicates, for every eight atoms of silicon there is one molecule of water.[17]) Much of this water is presumed to have been released from the crystalline heat-proof vault early in the Earth's history, squeezed out by heat and pressure in the mantle and outgassed from the mantle in volcanoes to create the primeval ocean. The amount of water in the Earth's mantle is, even today, probably *many times the mass of the oceans*.[18] Outgassing of water is also happening today. (Ninety-five percent of the gases extruded by volcanoes is water vapor from hydrated silicates; only about one percent is CO_2.[19])

Another potential source for Earth's water: comets. Vast amounts of water in the inner regions of the nascent hot Solar System, including those that might have outgassed from the primeval Earth, were driven with other volatiles to the frigid outer reaches of the solar system beyond the orbit of Neptune. There the water coalesced into icy comets in the Kuiper belt or the even more distant and mysterious Oort cloud. The water in the comets was safely stored—not in a heat-proof vault inside the Earth but in an icy refrigerator billions of miles from Earth—out of reach of the heat from the young Sun. It then returned to the inner regions of the young and chaotic solar system by crashing into the primeval Earth, delivering the precious water back to Earth. According to some geologists more than half the water on Earth was delivered in this way, by "comets on long sojourns far from their homes on the frigid outer margins of the solar system," Bjornerud explains. "Most comets have highly eccentric and elliptical orbits, and over time, many have made one-way trips into the inner solar system, unable to resist the gravitational charm of the planets."[20]

Bjornerud notes that the proportion "that is imported versus domestic is a controversial issue among geochemists."[21] Another point of controversy: Recent research is moving away from comets as a major exogenous source of Earth's water and towards asteroids.[22] In any case, the oceans and the Earth's vast depository of water are the result of the unique properties of water itself.

Maintaining Earth's Equipoise

FOR THE four billion years that the oceans have existed, the temperature over vast areas of the globe must have been more than 0°C and less than 100°C. Some of the environmental factors that have been responsible for the temperature stability and the preservation of the oceans over this vast period of time include the fact that the Sun's output of energy varies very little from year to year. Even over the great length of time since the oceans formed four billion years ago, the Sun's energy output has only changed by a relatively small amount, an increase of thirty percent.[23] Another contributing factor has been the stability of the Earth's orbit around the Sun. During all these billions of years, the orbit has remained steadfastly in the habitable zone, its stability enhanced by the size and motion of the Moon round the Earth. One estimate puts the odds of us having such a moon at more than eight percent.[24] Another puts its lower, at around two percent.[25] In either case, we are fortunate to have the Moon we have.

Earth has been fortunate in many other ways.[26] Cosmic, geometric, and geochemical considerations, and the relative constancy of the energy output of stars like the Sun, are certainly important elements of fitness in nature which have guaranteed the stability of Earth's hydrosphere for four billion years.

Despite our good fortune, Earth's temperature has fluctuated significantly throughout geological time; yet it has always returned after the fluctuations back to the long-term mean. This involved vast bodies of liquid water—the oceans—and temperatures between 0–100°C over a large proportion of the planet. The fluctuations are witnessed by the

FIGURE 3.4. ARIZONA METEOR CRATER.

succession of ice ages (some so severe that ice sheets may have extended to the tropics)[27] and periods of unusual warmth such as the Paleocene/Eocene Temperature Maximum (PETM), when the mean temperature of the Earth was 5 to 8°C warmer than today.[28] During the Cretaceous there were forests flourishing in high latitudes, and the world's mean temperature is estimated to have been several degrees higher than today. In addition to the ice ages and periods of increased warmth, there have been massive meteor strikes such as the one that hit the Yucatan Peninsula sixty-five million years ago, possibly ushering in the Cretaceous extinction event that ended the reign of the dinosaurs. Following this strike, the ejection of dust and the creation of various sunlight-absorbing aerosols in the atmosphere could have suppressed photosynthesis and cooled the Earth by (according to some estimates) up to 10°C for years or decades.[29]

Yet after each dramatic departure, the Earth's "equipoise" has always recovered and the climate restored to normal. As Bjornerud puts it, "Earth has had fevers and chills but has suffered no malady so extreme that its climatic immune system could not ultimately overcome it."[30]

Silicate Weathering

WATER PLAYS a central role in one of the most important of these immune systems, one that has protected the Earth from long-term temperature deviations over billions of years and preserved the oceans. This clever, elegant negative feedback regulatory system controls the world temperature by regulating the amount of CO_2 in the atmosphere through the weathering of silicate rocks.[31] As in so many other instances, this regulatory system is—to paraphrase the famous phrase of President Abraham Lincoln about the U.S. government—*of the water, by the water, and for the water.*

CO_2 is a greenhouse gas. It absorbs heat in the form of infrared radiation emitted by the Earth's surface, retaining it in the atmosphere and raising the temperature of both the hydrosphere and atmosphere. Water vapor is also a greenhouse gas and is responsible for retaining even more heat than CO_2, as discussed below.

If the CO_2 level *or* temperature falls, the rate of silicate weathering decreases, thereby increasing the amount of CO_2 in the atmosphere (from volcanism) and ultimately raising temperatures by the greenhouse effect. If the temperature or CO_2 levels rise, the rate of silicate weathering increases, reducing CO_2 levels and the resulting greenhouse effect, and lowering global temperatures. This intriguing *negative feedback* mechanism acts to lower or raise global temperatures and CO_2 levels in the atmosphere, returning the Earth to its long-term norm. By maintaining global temperatures near the current ambient range for billions of years, the mechanism has also played a vital role in the preservation of the oceans.

$$\uparrow$$
$$Mg_2SiO_4 + 4CO_2 + 4H_2O \rightleftharpoons 2MG^{2+} + 4HCO_3^- + H_4SiO_4 \quad (1)$$
$$\longrightarrow$$

OR

$$\text{olivine} + \text{carbon dioxide} + \text{water} \rightleftharpoons$$

$$\text{magnesium and bicarbonate ions in solution} + \text{silicic acid in solution}$$

This critical negative feedback system involves the chemical weathering of silicate rocks by carbonic acid. The diagram below shows that as CO_2 levels rise the reaction is drawn to the right.

The bicarbonate generated from atmospheric CO_2 is then carried to the oceans where marine microbes utilize it to manufacture the carbonate that composes their shells. The shells then rain to the sea bed as the organisms die—Rachel Carson's "stupendous snowfall." There it is sequestered in marine sediments, carrying the carbon dioxide from the atmosphere into the Earth as the oceanic crust subducts into the mantle. So the activities of living things are playing a critical role in this remarkable planetary immune system.[32]

The net effect is the removal of CO_2 from the atmosphere and the lowering of global temperatures.

On the other hand, if temperatures fall, then the rate of the reaction decreases and so too does the rate of removal of CO_2. The rate of the reaction is also decreased if the CO_2 falls, which again, decreases the extraction of CO_2 from the atmosphere and its burial in marine sediments. This allows CO_2 levels to start to creep back up and eventually causes the global temperature to rise again.

$$Mg_2SiO_4 + 4CO_2 + 4H_2O \rightleftharpoons 2Mg^{2+} + 4HCO_3^- + H_4SiO_4 \quad (1)$$

$\downarrow \qquad \longrightarrow$

Snowball Earth: A very dramatic example of how this regulatory system works is provided by the way the Earth warmed up and returned to normal to escape the ultra-cooling associated with a "snowball Earth," a period when ice caps extended right to the tropics and may well have covered the entire Earth's surface with a thick layer of ice. The key to the escape was the absence of silicate weathering. This allowed the CO_2 emitted from volcanoes to accumulate in the atmosphere above the ice, leading inevitably to an enhanced greenhouse effect, which warmed the Earth and led to a glacial retreat.[33]

Paleocene-Eocene Temperature Maximum: A dramatic instance of excessive atmospheric carbon dioxide being offloaded into marine sediments is found in a period following what is known as the Paleocene-Eocene Temperature Maximum (PETM).[34] During this temperature maximum massive amounts of CO_2 were released into the atmosphere, raising the global temperature by several degrees Celsius. But after a remarkably short period of geological time, silicate weathering, in conjunction with the burial of carbonates in the oceanic sediments and the newly formed oceanic crust, had returned the CO_2 and temperature levels to their long-term mean.

Avoiding a "Runaway Greenhouse": Silicate weathering has enabled the Earth to avoid the fate of Venus, which today has a dense atmosphere of ninety-six percent carbon dioxide, a surface pressure about ninety times that on Earth, a searing surface temperature of 475°C and no surface water.[35] Venus is, as Bjornerud recounts, a "hellish maelstrom where things have never settled into a routine." She continues:

> About the same size as Earth but closer to the Sun, Venus has always been hot. Mere proximity to the Sun, however, is not enough to account for the broiling weather on our sister planet, where it's 860°F and cloudy every day. The carbon dioxide and sulfur dioxide exhaled by its still-active volcanoes have turned Venus into an asphyxiating hothouse, because no reciprocal process removes these gases from the atmosphere at rates commensurate with their production. Earth would have met the same fate had it not devised a way to extract greenhouse gases [via silicate weathering] from the air and store them in sedimentary rocks.[36]

Being closer to the Sun was probably the major factor that doomed Venus to her hellish fate. Venus was hotter than Earth from the very beginning and may have lost her ocean early due to increased evaporation. In such a scenario, as the temperature of the Venusian atmosphere rose by the greenhouse effect, less and less water would have condensed out in the lower atmosphere. (On Earth, water vapor condenses because of intensely cold temperatures at high altitudes; see the section below on the "Cold Trap.") On Venus, water vapor would have instead risen into the upper atmosphere and been subjected to radiative splitting into hydrogen and oxygen. The hydrogen would then have escaped to space, eventually dehydrating the planet.[37] With its oceans lost, Venus had no water and hence no tectonic system to build "silicate mountains." It also had no means to bury excess carbon dioxide in the oceans as occurs on the Earth.

Another factor that may have hastened Venus' demise was the absence of life. Even if Venus once had oceans like Earth and even perhaps a nascent tectonic system, because it lacked life on land to assist with weathering and in the oceans to assist in the burial of carbon in marine sediments, CO_2 levels would have risen relentlessly and led to a runaway greenhouse effect.[38]

A Unique Homeostat

THE FIRST noticeable feature of the silicate feedback system or homeostat is the extraordinary number of ways the properties of water are playing a crucial role, working together to enable the mechanism to work.

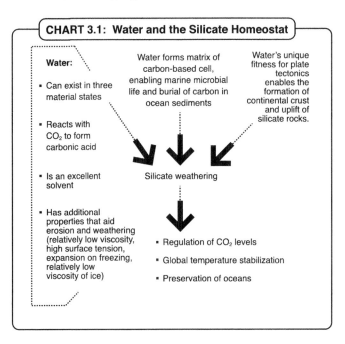

To begin with, (1) if water did not exist uniquely at least as a liquid and a gas in the ambient temperature range, the hydrological cycle would not turn and there would be no weathering of the rocks. And (2) if water did not form hydrated compounds with the silicates in the crust and mantle, reducing their viscosity and melting temperature, there would be no plate tectonics and no uplift of silicates in the continental crust for weathering. And (3) If water did not react with CO_2 to generate the carbonic acid that reacts with the silicates on the land, there would be no production of bicarbonate. And (4) if the solvation and erosional powers of water were less, then insufficient bicarbonate and silicic acid would be carried to the ocean for eventual burial.[39] And finally, (5) even the burial of the carbon and the removal of CO_2 from the hydrosphere and atmosphere by marine microorganisms and land plants is facilitated by water, as water is the matrix of all living cells on Earth.

Another remarkable feature of this regulatory system is that the major end of the system—temperature regulation (via fine-tuning the atmospheric level of CO_2)—has the inevitable consequence of conserv-

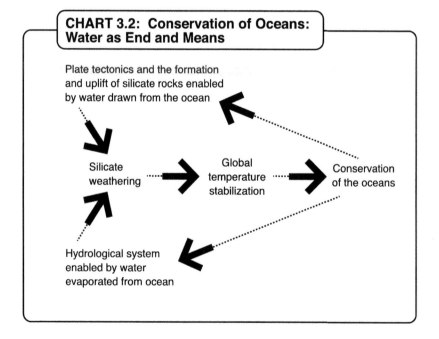

CHART 3.2: Conservation of Oceans: Water as End and Means

Plate tectonics and the formation and uplift of silicate rocks enabled by water drawn from the ocean

Silicate weathering

Global temperature stabilization

Conservation of the oceans

Hydrological system enabled by water evaporated from ocean

ing water (and the oceans) on Earth, and has probably done so for four billion years. But incredibly (and I think the word is well-chosen), it is water that is one of the agents, if not the main agent, responsible for the functioning of the homeostat itself. The vital end of the homeostat— conserving global temperature within the range in which water is a liquid, thereby conserving the oceans—is only achieved because of the vital agency of water itself in so many supportive roles. Such a homeostat is without any parallel in human engineering.

Simply put, the end is also the means of regulation of the end. A crude analogy might be an air conditioning system in which the product—cool air—is itself involved actively in the cooling process, or a missile for which the target is an active agent guiding the missile to its end. In fact, in all human-designed homeostats, guidance systems, or regulatory mechanisms, a complex device completely separate from the target or aim of the system achieves the regulatory goal. Here is another case where nature transcends artifact. In this, silicate weathering goes beyond the many other instances where water is mere end and means in some phenomenon or process. Here water is both end—maintaining temperature constancy and the oceans—and the means of regulating the end.

Truly the silicate-weathering homeostatic system is *of water, by water, for water.*

Parsimony: This remarkable regulatory system exemplifies another one of the *leitmotifs* of this book—that many of the processes and phenomena in which water is involved, such as the hydrological cycle, exhibit an extraordinary parsimony and elegance in serving more than one end. The erosion and weathering of the rocks (in which, as we saw in Chapter 1, a number of different properties of water work together in parallel to achieve the end) not only delivers the essential elements of life to the terrestrial hydrosphere but at the same time, as we have seen above, plays a role in regulating global temperature.

Wonder mounts as we recall that three of the reactants in silicate weathering—CO_2, water, and bicarbonate—are also fit to serve together in another vital process: human respiration (see Chapter 6). In the body, these three players form another ensemble, working together to rid the body of CO_2 *and* regulate the acidity of the blood.

Freezing from the Top Down

THE WAY the various properties of water, including its thermal properties, work together to preserve water in its liquid form on Earth represents a stunning example of an ensemble of mutual elements of fitness in the order of things. As in so many aspects of fitness, to comprehend the truly wonderful synergy involved, it is necessary to consider in some detail the way these various properties work together to the end of preserving water in its liquid form.

Expansion on Freezing: Unlike the vast majority of liquids, the volume of water expands when it freezes, so that the ice formed is lighter than water below and floats on the surface instead of sinking to the bottom. If it sank, the process of freezing would begin from the bottom up. The expansion of water on freezing is quite anomalous. Besides water, the only element that expands on freezing in the ambient temperature range is Gallium.[40] This property's fitness for life is clear. If water froze (as do nearly all other fluids) from the bottom up, the consequences would be severe in regions that experience persistent temperatures below 0°C (like the higher latitudes on Earth), or in cold eras when temperatures fall below 0°C over much of the globe, even in the equatorial regions (snowball Earth). The ice that formed on the bottom of cold bodies of water of any significant depth would be largely shielded from the warmth of the sun's rays. Such ice would not easily unfreeze, even on a sunny day. Eventually, virtually all the water on Earth would be frozen solid into vast masses of ice. Ice caps many kilometers deep would form at the poles, and in snowball Earth eras they would stretch right to the equator. The only liquid water in sight would be a transient film on top of vast ice sheets, and then only on particularly warm days. Simple life might survive such conditions by sporulating and awaiting more clement times, but complex life, both terrestrial and marine, would certainly be extinguished.

High heat capacity: When a body of water comes in contact with air below freezing and begins to cool, another element of fitness (line of defense) that comes into play to conserve water as a liquid (before it starts to freeze) is its high heat capacity, which is one of the highest to be found in any familiar liquid.[41] This acts to retard the rate of cooling. The relatively high heat capacity of water is observed in how long it takes to cool a cup of water compared to other equivalent materials in a household freezer. The rate of cooling would be much faster, and the tendency to freeze in cold weather much higher, if water had a lower heat capacity, similar to that of familiar substances such as metal or glass.

Maximal density at 4°C: As the temperature of the surface water cools toward freezing, yet another element of fitness comes into play: the curious and practically unique anomaly that the density of water is a maximum at 4°C and not at its freezing point, 0°C. (Virtually all other liquids are heaviest at their freezing point.) Consequently, as soon as the temperature of the surface waters cools to this temperature, 4°C, they sink to the bottom of the water column, out of reach of the freezing air at the surface.[42] Being lighter than the underlying heavy and slightly warmer water at 4°C, the coldest water is trapped in a layer at the surface. (This anomaly only applies to fresh water, not salt water—see note below.) And because the 4°C water sinks to the bottom, the cooling continues until the entire column of water from the bottom to the surface eventually attains this maximum density and a temperature of 4°C. Only then does the surface water finally begin to cool below 4°C, and finally to 0°C. This anomalous property of water further retards its tendency to freeze.

Latent heat of freezing: In addition, there is a fourth element of fitness acting towards the same end. As water finally solidifies, it gives out heat, technically the latent heat of fusion. The warming effect occurs because the molecular rearrangements that accompany freezing involve a decrease in energy, which is released during the phase change into the environment. In the case of water, this is again *anomalously high*, the highest of most familiar substances.[43] This heat is not released into the atmosphere, but absorbed by the liquid water just below the ice, buffering it against further temperature declines. Thus does the released heat act as another buffer, retarding the temperature decline and slowing the rate of cooling.

Low Heat Conductivity of Ice: Finally, after ice has formed, its insulating powers—a fifth property—retards further cooling of the water below. The conductivity of ice is low for a solid. Many metals, for example, have thermal conductivities orders of magnitude greater than that of ice.[44] As cooling continues, the protective ice sheet thickens, and with every increase in thickness the insulating effect of the ice grows more significant and the trapping of any latent heat of fusion in the water under the ice grows ever more effective. Eventually, no matter how cold the air above the water is, the layer of ice will not increase beyond a few meters thick.

The Viscosity of Ice: There is another surprising property of water that acts to conserve water in its liquid form on Earth: the relatively low viscosity of ice as a crystalline solid, many orders of magnitude lower than the viscosity of the minerals that make up the Earth's crust.[45] This ensures that most of the Earth's water is not locked up in vast accumulations of ice at the poles or in high mountainous regions. Because of its relatively low viscosity, unlike the rigid rocks of the crust, ice flows, so that in time all large accumulations of ice flow towards warmer temperatures downhill (valley glaciers) or outwards to the sea. There they inevitably melt, releasing liquid water again into the hydrosphere. Here is yet another property of water—this time a non-thermal property, which works together with its thermal properties to conserve liquid water on Earth.

Sea Water: The description above of the way water reacts to falling temperatures applies to bodies of fresh water—lakes and rivers. Although most of the unique thermal properties of water also apply to sea water, there is one major difference. *Unlike fresh water, the density of sea water continues to fall until the freezing point is reached, which in the case of sea water is about −1.8°C.*

The salt in sea water causes it to behave differently from fresh water, and not just by depressing the freezing point to below 0°C. Unlike fresh water, in which density and freezing point are determined by temperature alone, the density and freezing point of sea water is determined not only by temperature but also by the concentration of salt.

The differences have an important outcome. Because ice is lighter than water, as the temperature of sea water drops to –1.8°C (inevitable in the polar regions due to the frigid air above, which can be –30°C or less), thin patches of ice (grease ice) form on the surface. Salt is extruded from the ice as it freezes (anyone who has been to the Arctic will know that sea ice tastes much less salty than sea water), creating a cold and heavy brine[46] immediately under the surface of the ice.

The scale of brine production is immense, as Tom Garrison comments: "Salt is concentrated in pockets between crystals of pure water and then squeezed out of the freezing mass to form a frigid brine. Between 20 and 50 *million* cubic meters of this brine form every second [in the Antarctic]!"[47] This cold heavy brine is heavier than the underlying water, so it sinks to the ocean floor. As it sinks it warms slightly from its initial temperature of –1.8°C, but is still very cold. In fact, as Garrison points out, water at the bottom of the Antarctic has a temperature of –0.5°C and a density of 1.0279 grams/cc, which is the densest of any water in the world's oceans.[48]

The sinking stream of dense cold brine (which results from the unique properties of sea water and the extrusion of salt from ice) is one of the factors that initiates thermohaline circulation, an interconnected series of deep oceanic currents (see next chapter). Such currents are continually mixing and recycling the waters and nutrients of the world's oceans. Off the coast of Peru, the resulting Humboldt current causes an upwelling of nutrient-rich waters to the surface and fuels a massive proliferation of marine life.[49] So the different properties and behavior of sea water compared to fresh water turn out to be a crucial element of fitness. The thermohaline circulation promoted by the behavior of sea water also plays a role in ameliorating the Earth's climate (see next chapter).

Because of the intensely cold air above the polar waters, more and more patches of grease ice form and eventually coalesce, producing a thin layer of ice over the whole surface that gradually thickens to 1–1.5 meters in the Arctic.[50] The ice insulates and protects the water below from freezing further (in basically the same way as the layer of ice over frozen fresh water insulates the water below). So no more water freezes and life in the polar seas can continue to thrive no less than life under the ice in a freshwater lake or river.

The various convection movements in the oceans responsible for the thermohaline circulation are complex. They are influenced by many factors in addition to the formation and downwelling of the cold dense brine in the polar seas. These factors include the existence of distinct layers of sea water of different densities ("haloclines") and different temperatures ("thermoclines"[51]), which are present in the sea but not in bodies of fresh water.

Despite these intriguing differences in the behavior of fresh and sea water near their respective freezing points, the most important end result is the same: neither the polar seas nor freshwater lakes in high latitudes freeze from the bottom up.

So here, in one of the most familiar of natural phenomena, the freezing of both fresh and sea water, is an ensemble of unique elements of fitness, all working together to the same end of preserving water as a liquid. Many of the properties that ensure the preservation of water as a liquid are anomalous and depart from the norm seen in other liquids. This includes the expansion of fresh water below 4°C and the expansion of both fresh and sea water on freezing.

Although some other substances do share some of the thermal properties of water—ammonia, for example, has a slightly higher specific heat and higher heat of fusion,[52] and as mentioned above, a handful of other substances expand on freezing—*no fluid possesses a similar suite of properties that are mutually fit to work together towards the preservation of that fluid in the liquid state.*

Moreover, nature uses many of the same thermal properties of water to protect the oceans from excessive heating and evaporation and to ameliorate the climate (see next chapter).

And there is something more. Not only are these properties another stunning example of an ensemble of properties working together to a unique end (the preservation of the liquid state); they are also another example of water saving itself through its own properties, delivering itself by its own virtues to the land (Chapter 1), delivering itself to the primeval Earth, and acting itself as a prime agent to maintain the oceans for billions of years via the silicate-weathering homeostat. Again, no need for any extraneous control systems; water does it through its own unique properties.

The Cold Trap (Tropopause)

THE PROPERTIES discussed above do not exhaust the thermal properties of water that help to conserve water as a liquid on Earth. Yet another thermal property of water that contributes to its remarkable self-conservation is the relatively high temperature of the freezing and boiling points of water in comparison with other light hydrogen compounds and with atmospheric gases such as oxygen and nitrogen. (As mentioned in Chapter 1, this is due to the hydrogen-bonded network that confers a marked cohesiveness on water compared to many comparable liquids; see further discussion of the network in Chapter 7.)

At the top of the troposphere (the lower layer of the atmosphere), about ten kilometers above the Earth's surface, there is a layer called the tropopause, in which the air is intensely cold, way below the freezing point of water.[53] As Tim Lenton and Andrew Watson comment, at cruising altitude for commercial passenger airplanes "it is pretty chilly outside… typically minus fifty or sixty Celsius."[54] They add that these temperatures are "cold enough to freeze out virtually all the water in the air before it gets high enough to be split by solar UV."

Nitrogen and oxygen remain gaseous at intensely cold temperatures (well below minus sixty degrees Celsius), and can ascend high into the atmosphere. But because of its much higher freezing point, hardly any water ascends into the layer above the troposphere into the stratosphere.[55] The intense cold of the tropopause acts as a barrier, a "Cold Trap," that prevents water from ascending into the upper atmosphere where it would be subject to intense ultraviolet (UV) radiation. UV radiation dissociates water into hydrogen and oxygen, and because it is the lightest element, hydrogen would be lost to space. The result would be the eventual loss of the oceans and the complete dehydration of the Earth.

Lenton and Watson continue:

Without this atmospheric 'cold trap,' Earth would by now have lost much of its hydrogen to space and there might be no water left on the planet. This is what is thought to have happened to Venus, which is just as large as the Earth and is able therefore to retain the heavier gases, but which is too close to the Sun to have an efficient cold trap. All the water on Venus is thought to have dissociated and the hydrogen then escaped the planet, in a process called a 'runaway greenhouse.'[56]

Here is yet another case in which a property of water itself—the anomalously high temperature at which it freezes and vaporizes—conserves life's matrix on planet Earth.

Water Is a Greenhouse Gas

WE HAVE seen above that Earth has avoided a runaway greenhouse effect, probably due mainly to silicate weathering. Although a *runaway greenhouse* would be a catastrophe, some greenhouse effect is absolutely essential. Without greenhouse gases in the atmosphere, our planet would be a frozen world, a permanent snowball Earth. There would be no liquid water on the Earth's surface. The greenhouse gases, by retaining some of the incoming heat from the Sun and a fraction of the heat radiated from the Earth, raise the Earth's temperature by 33°C. Without the greenhouse gases, the average temperature on Earth would be a chilly –18°C, a little warmer than the Martian freezer but still too low for advanced terrestrial life.[57]

So which greenhouse gas do we most have to thank? It isn't carbon dioxide. The greenhouse gas in the Earth's atmosphere that makes nearly two-thirds of the contribution to retaining heat in the atmosphere is water.[58] Water as a gas has just the right physical properties to retain electromagnetic energy in the infrared region of the spectrum. And it is worth noting that nitrogen (N_2) and oxygen (O_2), which make up the bulk of the Earth's atmosphere and are necessary for any carbon-based biosphere, *are fortunately not greenhouse gases.* If they had been, the Earth might be a hellish hothouse, possibly hotter than Venus. Nitrogen and oxygen do not absorb energy in the infrared region.[59]

So water is a major greenhouse gas that makes the largest contribution to retaining atmospheric heat, maintaining our planet's temperature within the ambient range and conserving liquid water on Earth. This completes the astonishing number of diverse roles water plays in global environmental homeostasis and the conservation of the oceans.

Volume Control

IT IS not just that there has always been liquid water on Earth. There is also evidence that the volume of the oceans has changed little since their formation four billion years ago.[60] As Donald Wise pointed out some time ago, this means that there must be "various feedback mechanisms continually maintaining this fine adjustment between volume of ocean basins and volume of ocean waters."[61]

Remarkably, yet another unique property of water itself may be playing a role in the conservation of the volume of the seas by providing a novel feedback mechanism. Geoscientists James Kasting and Nils Holm have speculated that the regulation of the volume of the oceans involves the exploitation of a very remarkable property: the immense heat capacity of water close to the critical point.[62] The critical point is the temperature and pressure where liquid water and water vapor can coexist in equilibrium.[63] Extraordinary though it may seem, water at or close to its critical point has a heat capacity thousands of times greater than water at ambient temperatures[64] (see Figure 3.5). Because of this, water close

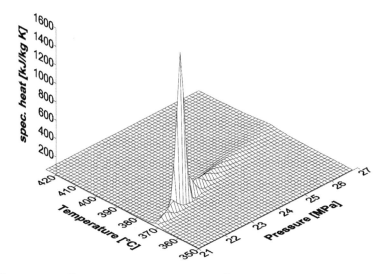

FIGURE 3.5. SPECIFIC HEAT OF WATER. SHOWING ENORMOUS PEAK AT CRITICAL POINT.

to its critical point is used as a coolant to transport heat away from the reactor core in nuclear power stations.[65]

Intriguingly, as Kasting and Holm point out, water in contact with the upwelling magma at the mid-ocean ridges (at a depth of about three thousand meters and three hundred times atmospheric pressure) is close to its critical point at a temperature of close to 400°C. It is therefore exceptionally fit to act as a cooling agent and to transport heat away from the newly forming oceanic crust.[66] This has an interesting consequence: it allows water to percolate far deeper into the newly forming oceanic crust than would otherwise be the case. Consequently, the crust carries more water from the oceans into the mantle at subduction zones. If the water level in the oceans drops so much that water at the ridges fails to reach its critical point, the hydration of the crust is reduced and less water is carried into the mantle during subduction. By this mechanism, according to Kasting and Holm, "The Earth's oceans may be determined by a dynamic mechanism involving an exchange of water between the crust and mantle."[67]

If this regulation mechanism does indeed play a role in conserving the volume of the world's oceans, then it represents yet another case where the conservation of water on Earth is being achieved by a unique property of water itself.

Chemical Stability

LAST BUT not least, another property of water which has played a crucial role in the persistence of vast quantities of water on Earth for billions of years is its great chemical stability in the presence of carbon dioxide, nitrogen, and oxygen, the three other basic constituents of the Earth's atmosphere and hydrosphere. (Carbon dioxide and nitrogen would be expected to be present in the atmosphere of any planet which harbored carbon-based life, and oxygen on any planet which harbored advanced metabolically active carbon-based life forms like humans.) Yet again, water saves itself on Earth by its own properties.

Its stability in the presence of oxygen is particularly significant for us, because only oxidations can provide sufficient energy to support the high metabolic rates necessary to support advanced complex carbon-based life forms.[68] Consequently, its very great stability in the presence of oxygen confers on water a unique and vital element of fitness for advanced carbon-based life. It is worth noting that few other liquids are as stable in the presence of oxygen, including several often cited as alternatives by authors defending the possibility of substitutes for water as the matrix for carbon-based life or for alternative biochemistries.[69]

Summary

IN THIS chapter, we have seen that the properties of water, more than any other factor, have conferred on Earth her miraculous ability to maintain her temperature within the ambient temperature range and to conserve her oceans over vast periods of time—to restore and maintain her "equipoise," as Bjornerud describes it. Ice ages have come and gone, and meteor strikes and massive volcanic eruptions have occurred. Following them, Earth for a time lost her equipoise, but water's amazing properties always managed to pull her through.

Water's role in this prime achievement is extraordinary, especially in those cases where liquid water has acted as an agent in its own preservation. Of course, the placement of Earth in the habitable zone, in a stable orbit in a stable solar system, has also played its role. But without water's talent for self-preservation, Earth's ability to support life would have vanished long ago!

Water is the crucial and ideal matrix of carbon-based life. That it should possess such a remarkable, indeed transcending, set of intrinsic properties that enable it to preserve *itself* in the liquid state on the surface the Earth, and to preserve the temperature of the environment within the ambient range, provides compelling evidence for the profound and unique fitness of water for life on Earth. Without water's self-preserving talents there would be no plate tectonics, no hydrological cycle, no oceans, no marine life, and certainly no advanced forms of terrestrial life such as ourselves.

CHART 3.3: Conservation of the Oceans: Water as End and Means

- High specific heat
- Expansion on freezing
- Maximum density at 4°C
- Latent heat of freezing
- Latent heat under ice
- Low heat conductivity of ice
- Low viscosity of ice
- High freezing and boiling points
- Silicate weathering
- Greenhouse effect

 Conserves liquid water on Earth

4. THE CLIMATE MACHINE

Earth is a very pleasant planet and, according to her stone diaries, has been so for millions of millennia. It is easy to forget just how remarkable this condition is, in the same way that we tend to be unaware of good health until becoming sick. For at least four billion years, through meteorite impacts, climate changes, and continental reorganizations, liquid water has remained stable at the Earth's surface, and life has thrived for nearly as long. Earth is a supersystem of countless smaller, interconnected systems involving rock, water, air, and life. These systems operate at spatial scales from microscopic to planetary, over time periods from seconds to millions of years… How did a messy tangle of systems without a centralized control mechanism (e.g., a brain, a band director, or a board of trustees) maintain Earth's equipoise over time?

Marcia Bjornerud, *Reading the Rocks* (2005)[1]

Water vapour is the strongest greenhouse gas, and the most variable component of the atmosphere. For these reasons, and because the transitions between the various phases absorb and release much energy, water vapour is central to the climate and its variability and change… The oceans cover approximately 70% of the Earth's surface. They store and transport a large amount of energy and dissolve and store great quantities of carbon dioxide. Compared with the atmosphere, their circulation is slow. They act as a regulator of the Earth's climate and also as a source of natural climate variability.

British Met Office website (2013)[2]

Benjamin Franklin learned of something puzzling while working as Deputy Postmaster General of North America, more than a decade before he became one of the founding fathers of the United States. English packet ships manned by English sailors carrying mail from Falmouth (at the southwestern tip of England) to New York took two weeks longer to make the journey than American merchant ships travelling from London to Rhode Island—a longer journey. From his cousin Captain Timothy Folger, a Nantucket sailor, Franklin learned

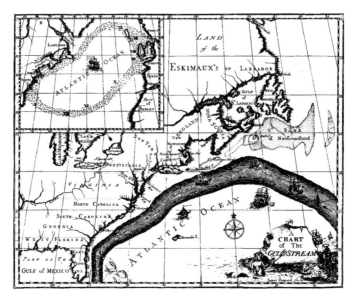

FIGURE 4.1. FRANKLIN'S MAP OF GULF STREAM.

that American merchants knew of a stream of fast flowing water that travelled eastwards across the Atlantic. They crossed the stream quickly on their journey from England to America to avoid sailing against the current. The English mariners, on the other hand, sailed within the stream and plied westward against the current, greatly lengthening their transit time across the Atlantic. With Folger, Franklin named the stream the Gulf Stream and published the first map showing its course in 1770.[3]

The Gulf Stream has a dramatic effect on the climate of western Europe and, through its offshoot, the North Atlantic Drift, on the climate of Norway and the Svalbard archipelago about eight hundred miles from the north pole.[4] Although northern parts of Norway are within the arctic circle, most of which is covered with ice and snow in winter, almost all of Norway's coast remains free of ice and snow throughout the year. Without the Gulf Stream, the British Isles and Norway—and certainly Svalbard—might be uninhabitable,[5] subject to an extremely cold climate like that of western Greenland.

What is the secret of the Gulf Stream's dramatic effect on the climate of north-western Europe? Once again, the cause lies in one of the properties of water. The very high specific heat of water enables the Gulf Stream to carry vast quantities of heat northward, more than the total amount of energy consumed by our global civilization[6] and far more than would be possible if water's specific heat was like that of most other familiar fluids.

Some have argued that heat stored in the oceans in the summer and released in the winter may be as important as or more important than the heat transported north by the Gulf Stream in ameliorating the wider climate in northwest Europe.[7] But this also depends on the great heat capacity of water.

Climatic Moderation

ONE NEEDS only take a nighttime dip in the sea on a warm summer day during a spell of anticyclonic weather (clear skies and no clouds) to experience first-hand the high heat capacity of water. At noon, when the temperature of the air may be around 30°C (86°F), the sea at 20°C (68°F), feels cool; but come evening of the same day, as the air temperature dips under a clear sky to 15°C (59°F), the sea is still 20°C—and now feels deliciously warm and inviting!

Specific heat: The sea is the same temperature as it was at noon due to its high heat capacity, which is about four times that of dry land (and twice that of wet land).[8] This buffers the sea against rapid temperature change compared to the land.[9] Moreover, the upper one hundred meters of the sea is continually in motion, being stirred or mixed, while the heat only penetrates a few meters into the land, which undergoes no convective mixing. As a result, the sea has an effective heat capacity one hundred times that of land.[10]

The buffering capacity of water's high specific heat (what Tom Garrison termed its "thermal inertia"[11]) is not only apparent to swimmers in the evening, but also very apparent in coastal regions bordering the world ocean. Coastal cities all over the world suffer far less diurnal[12] and year-to-year temperature change than cities located far inland, away from the moderating influence of the sea.[13] Further, coastal cities where the prevailing winds blow from the land, such as New York, have much greater annual changes in temperature than coastal cities like San Francisco, where the prevailing wind blows in from the Pacific Ocean.[14] Tom Garrison makes the point by comparing two other U.S. coastal cities:

> San Francisco, California, and Norfolk, Virginia are on the same line of latitude—each is the same distance from the equator. Wind tends to flow from west to east at this latitude.... Compared to Norfolk, San Francisco is warmer in the winter and cooler in the summer, in part because air in San Francisco has moved over the ocean while air in Norfolk has approached over land.[15]

As Mark Twain is credited with quipping, "The coldest winter I ever spent was a summer in San Francisco."[16]

And of course the stabilizing influence of the high specific heat of water has global implications. Garrison comments:

> Remember the hot sand and cool water on a hot summer afternoon? Think of the Earth as whole. The highest temperatures on land, in the north African desert, exceed 50°C (122°F); the lowest, on the Antarctic continent, drop below –90°C (–129°F). That's a difference of 140°C (250°F)! On the ocean surface, however, the range is from 2°C (29°F) where sea ice is forming to about 32°C (90°F) in the tropics—a difference of only 34°C (61°F). Consisting of water, the ocean rises very little in temperature as it absorbs heat. The ocean's thermal inertia is much greater than the land's.[17]

Latent Heat of Evaporation and Condensation: The other thermal property of water that contributes greatly to its climatic moderating powers is the cooling effect of its very high latent heat of evaporation, *the highest of any molecular fluid.*[18] The cooling effect when water evaporates is also an everyday experience. Even on the warmest day, the slightest breeze can make the skin feel very cool when drying off after a swim. And the cooling effect of evaporation prevents a swimming pool from heating up on the hottest of days if there is even a minor breeze.

The cooling effect of evaporation buffers the temperature of all bodies of water on Earth, from small lakes to the Pacific Ocean (and adjacent land areas), against rapid temperature increases when the ambient temperature rises. If it were not for the high evaporative cooling effect —despite the high heat capacity of water—small bodies of water in the tropics would have no way of ridding themselves of heat and would relentlessly heat up during the day to temperatures of 40°C, 50°C, or more. This would virtually eliminate all complex aerobic life, because the solubility of oxygen in water declines rapidly with temperature; at 50°C the solubility is one third that at 0°C and thirty percent less than at 30°C[19]. It would empty the tropical lakes and rivers of fish, leaving only primitive unicellular organism and extremophiles to thrive in the toxic, hot, anoxic waters.

Conversely, the rate of environmental temperature fall is slowed wherever there is any water vapor in the atmosphere, because as water vapor in the atmosphere condenses, the latent heat is liberated and warms the air. A second factor at play, also involving water: On cloudy nights, clouds reflect back to the ground some of the infrared radiation emitted up from the ground. Together, these two effects make for a big difference. We have all experienced the curious warming effect of humid conditions and cloud cover. On a clear, cloudless winter night in the higher latitudes, the temperature may drop to far below freezing. But in cloudy conditions even in deep winter, the temperature may remain well above freezing all night.

The cooling effect when water evaporates into a gas and the warming effect when it condenses back into a liquid (the two consequences of its high latent heat) play a major role in the climate machine and in the transfer of heat from the tropics to the higher latitudes (see below).

The fitness of the evaporative cooling effect in moderating climatic conditions (and in cooling the human body, as we shall see in Chapter 6) is wonderfully enhanced by the fact that this effect intensifies with increasing temperature. As temperatures rise, more water evaporates and more water vapor enters the atmosphere, enhancing the cooling of the

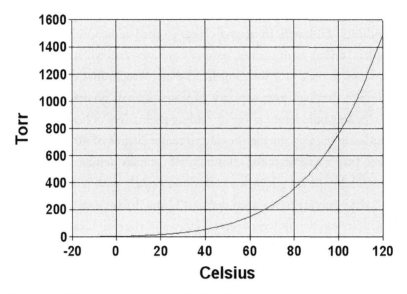

FIGURE 4.2. VAPOR PRESSURE (MM HG) V. TEMPERATURE.

atmosphere (see Figure 4.2). In other words, the cooling effect is greatest when it is needed most. In effect, it acts as a negative feedback system! It is easy to envisage the inconvenience if the reverse were the case, in a counterfactual world where evaporative cooling increased with decreasing temperatures. Such a positive feedback effect would be massively dysfunctional!

The Latent Heat of Freezing: The third thermal property of water that plays an important role in climatic moderation is its latent heat of freezing. As mentioned in Chapter 3, it is the highest of most familiar substances. This has the effect of attenuating temperature falls through the release of heat as water freezes and conversely attenuating temperature rises by absorbing heat as ice and snow melts.

Whewell on the Fitness of Latent Heat: William Whewell was one of the first authors to provide a clear account of the fitness for climatic moderation of the high latent heat associated with the water's phase transitions from ice to water and from water to steam, exploring the matter in his Bridgewater Treatise entitled *Astronomy and General Physics Considered with Reference to Natural Theology* (1834).[20] His insights on the subject are perceptive and still impressive nearly two centuries later. I have taken the liberty of quoting him at length:

> There is a peculiar circumstance still to be noticed in the changes from ice to water and from water to steam. These changes take place at a particular and invariable degree of heat; yet they do not take place suddenly when we increase the heat to this degree. This is a very curious arrangement. The temperature *makes a stand*, as it were, at the point where thaw, and where boiling take place. It is necessary to apply a considerable quantity of heat to produce these effects; all which heat disappears, or becomes *latent*, as it is called. We cannot raise the temperature of a thawing mass of ice till we have thawed the whole. We cannot raise the temperature of boiling water, or of steam rising from it, till we have converted all the water into steam. Any heat which we apply while these changes are going on is absorbed in producing the changes.

> The consequences of this property of *latent heat* are very important. It is on this account that the changes now spoken of necessarily occupy a considerable time. Each part in succession must have a proper degree of heat applied to it. If it were otherwise, thaw and evaporation must be instantaneous: at the first touch of warmth, all the snow which lies on the roofs of our houses would descend like a waterspout into the streets: all that which rests on the ground would rush like an inundation into the water courses. The hut of the Esquimaux would vanish like a house in a pantomime: the icy floor of the river would be gone without giving any warning to the skaiter or the traveller: and when, in heating our water, we reached the boiling point, the whole fluid would "flash into steam"… and dissipate itself in the atmosphere, or settle in dew on the neighbouring objects.

> It is obviously necessary for the purposes of human life, that these changes should be of a more gradual and manageable kind than such as we have now described. Yet this gradual progress of freezing and thawing, of evaporation and condensation, is produced, so far as we can discover, by a particular contrivance. Like the freezing of water from the top, or the floating of ice, the moderation of the rate of these changes seems to be the result of the *violation* of a law: that is, the simple rule regarding the effects of change of temperature, which

at first sight appears to be the law, and which, from its simplicity, would seem to us the most obvious law for these as well as other cases, is modified at certain critical points, *so as to* produce these advantageous effects: —why may we not say *in order* to produce such effects?[21] [emphasis in original]

Whewell concludes: "The uses of those arrangements... are well suited to give confidence and hope to our researches for such usefulness in every part of the creation. They have thus a peculiar value in adding connection and universality to our perception of beneficial design."[22]

What is particularly fascinating is the way these various thermal properties—specific heat, high latent heat of freezing and melting, and the high latent heat of evaporation and condensation—work together with such synergic panache to achieve the same end of temperature inertia and climatic moderation! And as we shall see below, these same thermal properties are involved both in the great climate machine and in the maintenance of temperature homeostasis in warm-blooded organisms like ourselves.

The Global Climate Machine

As a sphere circulating its sun, geometry dictates that Earth's higher latitudes receive less radiation per unit area than the equatorial regions where the Sun's rays are more nearly perpendicular to the surface. Indeed, the higher latitudes have a negative heat balance, while in the tropics the situation is reversed.[23] While the thermal properties of water do indeed buffer *local* environments against short-term temperature changes, in themselves they would still leave much of the Earth either too hot or too cold.

Unless there were large-scale convection mechanisms transferring heat from hot tropical regions to the cooler higher latitudes, i.e., poleward from the equator, the Earth would be a very inclement place. Calculations show that without heat transfer, despite the thermal properties of water the average temperature in the equatorial regions would be 14°C hotter and the poles 25°C colder.[24] The middle latitudes—where many major population centers such as New York, London, and Beijing are located—might be covered in ice.[25] Without convective mechanisms to transfer heat from the tropical regions to the higher latitudes, many parts of the Earth, especially continental regions in the tropics, would be unlivably hot while continental regions in the middle to high latitudes would be inhospitably cold.

This convectional heat transfer involves the integrated actions of a number of diverse mechanisms of which few people (apart from professional climatologists) are aware: Hadley cells, Ferrel cells, polar cells, the thermohaline circulation, wind-blown gyres, Ekman spirals, the Coriolis force, the meridional overturning circulation (MOC), planetary albedo, and the so-called "Ocean Conveyor Belt."[26] All these mechanisms are components of what is often termed the *climate system* or *climate machine*. And the central player that enables the convective transfer to occur is, once again, water.

And again, the high specific heat of water and its high latent heat of evaporation and condensation play crucial roles.

Atmospheric Heat Transport

THE CONVECTIVE mechanisms that moderate the temperature differences between different regions of the Earth consist of both atmospheric currents and ocean currents, such as the Gulf Stream. Together, they transport vast quantities of heat from the warm equatorial and tropical regions to the cooler higher latitudes.[27] About sixty-six percent of the heat is transported poleward in the atmosphere and thirty-three percent in ocean currents.[28] Altogether the amount of heat transferred from the tropics to the higher latitudes is sufficient *to warm all the higher latitudes of the Earth by several degrees Celsius.*[29]

Hadley, Ferrel, and polar cells are major mechanisms of atmospheric heat transport poleward. In the Hadley cell, warm air rises at the equator until it reaches the tropopause, then moves northward to the thirtieth latitude, where it falls down to the surface and flows back to the equator. In the polar cell, air rises at the sixtieth latitude until it reaches the tropopause, then it moves northward to the pole, where it falls down

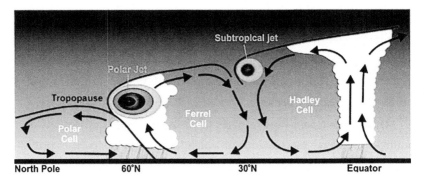

North Pole 60°N 30°N Equator

FIGURE 4.3. THE HADLEY, FERREL, AND POLAR CELLS.

to the surface. In the Ferrel cell, caught between the Hadley and polar cells, air rises near the sixtieth latitude and moves southward to the thirtieth latitude, where it drops down to the surface and moves northward. So the Hadley cell transports heat poleward in the upper atmosphere and the Ferrel cell transports heat poleward in the lower atmosphere (see Figure 4.3).

In the Hadley cell, warm air containing water vapor that has evaporated from the tropical seas rises from the surface into the upper atmosphere. As the air flows between the equator and the thirtieth latitude in the upper atmosphere, it cools and the water vapor condenses as rain, releasing latent heat collected when it evaporated at the equator. It thereby carries heat from the tropics toward the poles.

The critical role played by the high latent heat of evaporation in maintaining global temperature equity and moderation was not lost on Lawrence Henderson:

> At the equator the evaporation of the ocean appears to be about 2.3 meters per year... The effect of this enormous evaporation to moderate the temperature of the tropics is very considerable; but the heat which thus disappears is not lost. Rendered latent at the place of evaporation, it is turned back into actual heat at the point of condensation, and thus serves to warm another and cooler locality... No other liquid could, during the evaporation of a given quantity

of material, bind so much heat; no other vapor could yield so much heat upon condensation.[30]

Although some sensible heat is also transported in the atmosphere, the transport of heat is overwhelmingly dependent on the latent heat of evaporation and condensation of water. Without water's very high latent heat of evaporation and condensation, and the atmospheric transport of heat toward the polar regions, the convective redistribution of heat would be greatly diminished.

Not only is water vapor carrying warmth poleward by storing it as latent heat, but the latent heat of evaporation and condensation is also playing a major role by driving the circulation of the air and forming the atmospheric currents themselves.[31] As the authors of a study of the influence of water's latent heat of evaporation on Hadley cell circulation comment, "The release of latent heat plays an essential role in driving the general circulation of the atmosphere."[32] As Tapio Schneider, Paul O'Gorman, and Xavier Levine stress:

> Water vapor is not only important for Earth's radiative balance as the dominant greenhouse gas of the atmosphere. It is also an active player in dynamic processes that shape the global circulation of the atmosphere and thus climate. The latent heat released when atmospheric water vapor condenses and the cooling of air through evaporation or sublimation of condensate affect atmospheric circulations. Although the mechanisms are not well understood, it is widely appreciated that heating and cooling of air through phase changes of water are integral to moist convection and dynamics in the equatorial region.[33]

Trades and Prevailing Westerlies: The atmospheric currents set in motion by the Hadley cells generate the celebrated *trade winds* that blow from northeast to southwest in the Northern Hemisphere, and from the mid-latitudes to the subtropics. (These same winds carried Columbus across the Atlantic from the Canary Islands to landfall in the new world in only thirty-six days.[34]) The Hadley cells also interact with the Ferrel cells which are responsible for the prevailing westerlies in the mid-

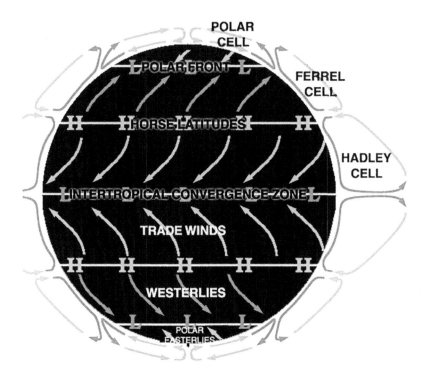

FIGURE 4.4. ATMOSPHERIC CIRCULATION SHOWING TRADES AND WESTERLIES.

latitudes. Both winds blow in reverse directions in the Southern Hemisphere (see Figure 4.4).

The predominant westward direction of the trade winds is determined by the Coriolis force. This is an apparent force which acts on moving objects on the surface of a rotating body such as the Earth. In the case of the Earth, which is rotating from west to east, it causes moving objects to be deflected to the right in the Northern Hemisphere, and to the left in the Southern. Thus, in the Northern Hemisphere, as the surface air in the Hadley cell proceeds southward, the Coriolis force causes it to move northeast to southwest (the northeasterly trade winds), while the same force causes northward-proceeding surface air in the mid-latitude Ferrel cell to move southwest to northeast (the southeasterly trades).

These great atmospheric currents not only moderate Earth's climate, but also carry rain-bearing weather systems over the continental areas—a vital activity upon which many critical processes, such as the hydrological cycle, depend. If it were not for the rain-bearing clouds borne inland by these prevailing winds, there would be less rain in most continental regions of the globe, and the effectiveness of the hydrological cycle would be very much diminished.

The Ocean Conveyor Belt

As MENTIONED above, about two thirds of the tropical heat transferred poleward is carried in the atmosphere via atmospheric currents—the *Hadley* and *Ferrel* cells, the trade winds, and the westerlies. The remaining third is carried by the great ocean currents.[35] There are two types of ocean currents: wind-driven *surface currents* or gyres (shown in Figure 4.5), and *deep currents*, which make up what is called the thermohaline circulation, an interconnected global network of deep submarine currents.[36]

Surface currents: The persistent blowing of the trades and westerlies over the surface of the ocean generates what climatologists term "the great gyres," vast cyclic movements of water. The Gulf Stream is part of the *North Atlantic Gyre*, which takes warm water from the Caribbean up the east coast of North America. There, it gives rise to the North Atlantic Drift, which carries warm water further north to the west coast of Norway and the Svalbard archipelago (see Figure 4.5). The Humboldt Current, which transports cold Antarctic water along the west coast of South America to the warm tropical Pacific, is part of the *Pacific Gyre*. Thus, by carrying cold water towards the equator (the Humboldt), or warm water towards the poles (the Gulf Stream), the great ocean currents play their role in the convectional transfer of heat, moderating further the temperature gradient imposed on the Earth by its spherical form and the unequal distribution of the Sun's radiant energy at different latitudes.

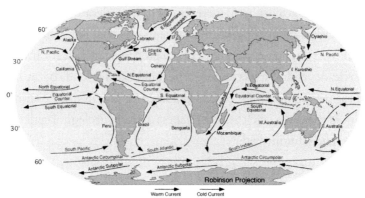

FIGURE 4.5. SURFACE OCEAN CURRENTS.

The heat transported in these great, wind-driven, surface ocean cur-rents is considerable. Their importance in heat transport was understood in 1913 by Lawrence Henderson. About the Gulf Stream, he comments:

> In the Straits of Yucatan the Gulf Stream carries 0.2 cubic kilome-ters (200,000,000 tons) per second. If all this water were to be cooled to the temperature of the polar ocean this would be the equivalent to the transport of about 5,000,000,000,000,000 gram calories per second. The magnitude of this quantity, of course, depends upon the specific heat of water.[37]

A more recent estimate in *Nature* of the rate at which heat is car-ried in the Gulf Stream gave a figure in the order of 10^{15} Watts,[38] which (as mentioned above) is more than the current power consumption of human civilization. This enormous figure is a massive testimony to the heat capacity of water! With so much heat transported poleward, it is small wonder that recent computer simulations show that if it were not for the heat carried poleward by the ocean surface currents the northern hemisphere would be quite different. According to Geoffrey Vallis, "The simulations without oceanic heat transport all developed large ice sheets that covered mid- and high latitudes, making the overall climate much colder than it is now."[39]

That these ocean currents can carry such vast amounts of heat around the planet is of course due to the very high specific heat or heat capacity of water. But water's viscosity and density also play an important role. The viscosity and density of water must be approximately what they are or the ocean currents would be impossible. Were water as viscous as treacle, the oceans would be immobile. There would be no waves and no surf. Even if winds did blow across such a viscous ocean, there would be no gyres to ameliorate the climate.

Deep Ocean Currents: All continuous flows of air in the atmosphere or of water in the oceans (Hadley and Ferrel cells, the surface gyres, etc.) must ultimately be cyclical—neither air nor water can flow continually in one direction. As Figure 4.5 shows, the great gyres are essentially horizontal circular movements of water. But the horizontal surface circulation is enhanced by another type of circulation: a vertical circulation that involves downwelling of surface water in one part of the world ocean and upwelling in another. The downwelling streams are linked with the upwelling streams in a vast set of ocean bottom currents known as the thermohaline circulation. Thus the downwelling of cold, heavy water in the polar regions in the north Atlantic plays a role in enabling the Gulf Stream, while upwellings of cold, deep water as it courses north from the southern part of South America along the coast of Chile and Peru enables the Humboldt Current (see Figure 4.6).

The figure shows very simply how a surface current generated by wind (in this case the Humboldt Current), that pushes surface water continu-

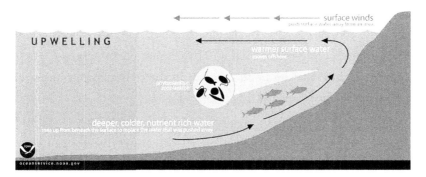

FIGURE 4.6. UPWELLING OF DEEP OCEAN WATER AND THE HUMBOLDT CURRENT.

ally in one direction, can cause a complementary upwelling of deep ocean water, by drawing or pulling water up from the ocean depths and causing a deep ocean current. On the other hand, in the case of the Gulf Stream, as mentioned above it is the downwelling of cold heavy brine in the north Atlantic that *pulls* the warm waters of the Gulf Stream north.[40]

As noted in the previous chapter, where the process is described in more detail, the primary cause of the sinking of the water is that the density of sea water continues to increase all the way to −1.8°C, promoting the downwelling of cold polar sea water. Here again, as in so many of the properties of water, it is hard to escape the impression that water is specially fit to serve very specific ends aiding life on Earth. If sea water were maximally dense at 4°C, its surface water likely would still sink, but the resulting circulation would be far less vigorous and effective. With weaker downwelling, the surface currents would be greatly constrained and the moderating effect of the ocean currents would cease. New York City might indeed be covered in ice, and not just during the occasional winter storm.

Currently, some climatologists are worried that if global warming continues, it might prevent the cooling of the surface waters in the North Atlantic that causes the downwelling of cold, dense water that pulls the warm Gulf Stream waters north. The fear is that this would have catastrophic effects on the climate of northwest Europe and North America.[41]

But whether this dire prediction is realistic or not, there is no doubt that an apparently esoteric and unique property of sea water plays a critical role in enabling the circulation of the great ocean currents. These currents in turn play an important role in the convectional transfer of heat from the tropics to the higher latitudes.

Mixing and Stirring: In addition to enhancing the flow of the surface currents, the deep ocean currents do something else. They mix and stir the waters of the world ocean, keeping them fresh and redistributing their dissolved mineral content and nutrients. This is spectacularly manifest in the case of the Humboldt Current, where the upwelling of nutrients from the ocean depths causes a vast proliferation of marine life,[42] unequalled anywhere else on Earth.

Evidence for the critical role of thermohaline circulation in keeping the seas fresh and hospitable to life by stirring and mixing can be seen in tropical lakes. Because the surface waters never cool to any significant degree, water circulation is much less, and on occasion this may lead to a dangerous build-up of gases in the depths of the lake. This occurred in 1986 at Lake Nyos in Africa, when a sudden release of CO_2 from the bottom of the lake produced a disastrous cloud of asphyxiating gas, killing over one thousand people.[43]

William Cromie, science writer and long-time contributor to the *Harvard Gazette*, succinctly summed up the contribution of the ocean currents to the well-being of the seas and Earth's climate:

> Subtle differences in temperature and salinity cause density variations which can move whole oceans, horizontally and vertically. It is these variations, together with the forces of wind and gravity that distribute the salts of the sea evenly, that moderate temperatures on our planet and mix together all the water of the world ocean.[44]

Summary

A TRULY remarkable aspect of the climate machine is that the thermal properties of water—the latent heat of evaporation in the atmosphere and its specific heat capacity in the oceans—are at the heart of the entire system, doing most of the work of transporting and redistributing heat around the globe. If either of these two properties did not have the values they do, the entire climate machine would grind to a halt, permanent ice might cover the region where New York currently stands, and all tropical regions would be hellishly hot.

So the thermal properties of water help produce the atmospheric currents (via Hadley and Ferrel cells) that contribute to ocean currents, which also use water's thermal properties to better redistribute heat. The *end*—the transport of heat—is achieved by the *means* of the thermal properties of water.

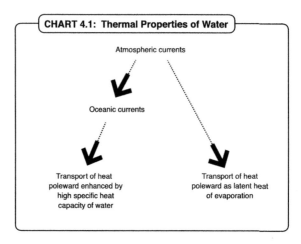

CHART 4.1: Thermal Properties of Water

Atmospheric currents

Oceanic currents

Transport of heat poleward enhanced by high specific heat capacity of water

Transport of heat poleward as latent heat of evaporation

If the various properties of water were much different, if its heat capacity and latent heat of evaporation were not anomalously high, the climate machine could not work its moderating magic. There would be no Hadley or Ferrel cells, no prevailing winds such as the trades and the westerlies, and no ocean currents. And if the viscosity of water were much higher, the ocean currents would grind to a halt. Moreover, if the maximum density of sea water were the same as that of fresh water, the downwelling of the polar seas would cease and many of the surface currents would be greatly constrained.

There is no doubt that the climate machine is beneficial to all life on Earth. The upwelling and mixing of the ocean waters promotes a massive abundance of marine life in various parts of the ocean. The great weather systems driven by the prevailing winds carry vast quantities of water to the land, enhancing the hydrological cycle and promoting terrestrial life. But it is hard to argue that all aspects of the climate machine are essential for life on Earth, since simple microbial life could survive under much harsher conditions. The moderation of the climate must therefore be judged to be to some degree *gratuitous*, ameliorating greatly the environmental conditions on Earth especially for complex advanced life forms. Such gratuity serves to confirm further that the fabric of things is fit for beings like ourselves, not just for carbon-based life generally.

5. WATER, TREES, AND LIGHT

Think of the Sun's heat on your upturned face on a cloudless summer's day; think how dangerous it is to gaze at the Sun directly. From 150 million kilometers away, we recognize its power. What would we feel on its seething self-luminous surface, or immersed in its heart of nuclear fire? The Sun warms us and feeds us and permits us to see. It fecundated the Earth. It is powerful beyond human experience. Birds greet the sunrise with an audible ecstasy. Even some one-celled organisms know to swim to the light. Our ancestors worshipped the Sun, and they were far from foolish.

Carl Sagan, *Cosmos* (1985)[1]

It may form an interesting intellectual exercise to imagine ways in which life might arise, and having arisen might maintain itself, on a dark planet; but I doubt very much that this has ever happened, or that it can happen.

George Wald, *Scientific American* (1959)[2]

THE DELIGHTFUL ANTICS OF POND SKATERS AND WHIRLIGIG BEE-tles gyrating across the surface of a pond depend entirely on the fact that of all familiar liquids (apart from mercury) water has the highest surface tension.[3] These tiny denizens of the interface of water and air would sink if they tried these same antics on alcohol or any other familiar liquid. It is ultimately, again, water's hydrogen-bonded network that confers on water its high surface tension as well as its unique cohesiveness, its solvation powers, and its existence as a liquid at ambient temperatures.

The fitness of water's high surface tension for a pond skater's or whirligig beetle's way of life may seem somewhat trivial alongside the fitness of water for the hydrological cycle, for softening the mantle rocks, for preserving the oceans, and for regulating the temperature of the Earth. But it's not only these little creatures that benefit. As we saw in Chapter

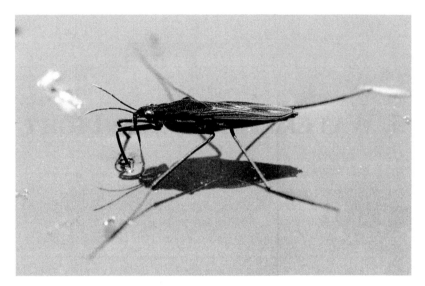

FIGURE 5.1. POND SKATER.

1, water's high surface tension enhances erosion and weathering, and allows the formation of soil by drawing water into narrow rock fissures where it can fragment the rocks upon freezing. Thus does water's high surface tension, working in conjunction with other properties of water, assist in leaching key minerals and nutrients from rocks and delivering them to terrestrial biotas.

As we also saw in Chapter 1, water's high surface tension also promotes the growth of terrestrial plants by drawing water by capillary action through the soil within easy reach of the roots of plants. Lawrence Henderson underscored the point in his classic *The Fitness of the Environment*: "The principal factor in bringing water within reach of plants is the exceptional surface tension of water.... The rise of water in capillary systems resembling soil, under the action of surface tension, may be as much as ten feet."[4]

Trees: Mirabile Dictu!

SURFACE TENSION not only draws water through the soil, but also plays a key role in the mechanism of drawing water to the top of plants and even to the top of tall trees. The drawing of water to the top of tall trees is no

FIGURE 5.2. COASTAL REDWOODS.

trivial or esoteric element of fitness, as it was the wood provided by trees which played an indispensable role in mankind's mastery of fire. This was the first critical and fateful step taken by our ancestors towards the smelting of metals from their ores and the subsequent development of metallurgy and advanced technology. Wood (or charcoal, a wood product) is the only suitable reduced carbon fuel for the high-temperature fire needed for metallurgy.[5]

Steven Vogel, in his book *The Life of a Leaf*, describes the way water manages to get to the top of tall trees as a tale *mirabile dictu* ("wonderful to relate").[6] It turns out that this feat depends not only on the high surface tension of water but also, because of another unusual property of water, its remarkable and counterintuitive *tensile strength*, which like its high surface tension is also the result of its hydrogen-bonded network.

Simple capillarity caused by surface tension (a generic property of all fluids) can easily lift water up to one hundred meters if the tube is small enough. In tubes one hundredth of a micrometer (ten nanometers) in diameter, the surface tension is so strong that it can support a column of water three kilometers (about two miles) high.[7] But because of viscosity (a measurement of internal friction), water's resistance to flowing through such tiny conduits would be prohibitively high.[8] The conduits in trees are between 0.03 and 0.3 millimeters (i.e., between 30 and 300 micrometers) in diameter, sufficiently wide to allow the water to flow up through the tubes with minimal resistance. But as Vogel comments, "Thirty micrometers sends water only about 1.5 meters (5 feet) upward, and 300 micrometers is ten times worse: 15 centimeters, or 6 inches."[9] So how do trees manage to exploit capillarity to hold a column of water one hundred meters high (requiring tiny tubes) while at the same time overcoming viscous drag?

As Michele Holbrook and Maciej Zwieniecki explain, plants solve the problem of the viscous drag "by connecting the small capillaries in leaves [which are small enough to generate capillary forces powerful enough to hold a column 100 m high] to larger ones that provide a much wider transport channel that runs from the veins in the leaf down through the stem and into the roots."[10]

The key point is that the critical capillary forces are not generated in the major conduits. As Holbrook and Zwieniecki point out:

> The relevant capillary dimensions are not those of the relatively large conduits that you would see if you cut down a tree and looked inside... (diameters of 50–100 μm) Rather, the appropriate dimensions are determined by the air-water interfaces in the cell walls of the leaves, where the matrix of cellulose microfibrils is highly wettable and the spacing between them results in effective pore diameters [which function as tiny capillaries] of something like 5–10 nm.[11]

And this is the crucial point: the pore diameter is so small that the surface tension generated (as mentioned above) is able to support a water column three kilometers high, much higher than the highest tree.

In other words, as the same authors continue:

> Trees and other plants overcome... [the problem] by generating capillary forces in small-diameter pores [at the interfaces in the leaves between the sap and the air] but transporting water between soil

and leaves through larger-diameter conduits. That strategy allows them to achieve greater heights than with a straight-walled micro-capillary.[12]

It is worth noting again that the low viscosity of water plays a vital role. If the viscosity were much higher, the conduits between root and leaf might take up an incommensurate volume of the trunk!

But while capillarity suffices to hold up the hundred-meter column, what pulls the water up from the roots through the conduits to the stems and leaves at the top of the tree? The answer is that the evaporation or transpiration from the air-water interfaces in the leaf cell produces suction by inducing a negative pressure in the fluid under the tiny menisci, which is transmitted to the whole system of conduits. It is a basic law of hydraulics that pressure in one part of an enclosed hydraulic system is transmitted to all other parts. As water molecules are lost from the leaves at the top of the tree, others must enter the roots to take their place. The continual loss of water molecules lowers what is termed the *water potential* in the regions below the interfaces. (*Water potential* is a measure of water's tendency in a given context to migrate from one place to another due to one or more factors—factors such as capillary action, osmosis, or gravity.)

This lowering of potential, transmitted to the whole hydraulic network, pulls the water up the conduits to the interfaces where it is lost by evaporation to the atmosphere.

An obvious question arises: Why does the column of water not break into pieces as it is tugged from above? The answer lies in the cohesiveness of liquids mentioned earlier, more pronounced in water than in most other common fluids. Water's hydrogen bonded network at work again! And because of this property of water columns, although the notion is very counter intuitive, water in the conduits has *tensile strength*.[13]

Tensile strength is the ability of a substance to resist being stretched. You can pull a steel wire up one hundred meters without breaking it because of the tensile strength of steel. Curiously, it is the same with a water column. As Vogel points out, experiments show that a rope of liquid water, a square centimeter in cross-section in an enclosed tube, has sufficient tensile strength to support a solid mass of nearly three hundred kilograms.[14] And as Vogel points out, although steel is stronger, it is only ten times as strong! It is this very counterintuitive tensile strength of fluids—especially water—that allows the negative pressure caused by the evaporation in the leaves to pull water from the roots one hundred meters up to the leaves without any breakage in the column.

This remarkable mechanism, so vital to the existence of large trees, depends critically on two basic physical properties of water as a fluid: its tensile strength, which means the "pull of evaporation" will not break the water column; and the enormous surface tension generated by water in very narrow tubes or passages.

The mechanism represents a unique and stunningly brilliant solution to the problem of raising water to the top of large trees. Significantly, no conceivable alternative will work. Vogel in his *The Life of a Leaf* waxes lyrical in contemplating the way it's done: "The pumping system has no moving parts, costs the plant no metabolic energy, moves more water than all the circulatory systems of animals combined, does so against far higher resistance, and depends on a mechanism with *no close analogy in human technology*."[15]

Holbrook and Zwieniecki concur:

Trees can be rightly called the masters of microfluidics. In the stem of a large tree, the number of interconnected water transport conduits can exceed hundreds of millions, and their total length can be greater than several hundred kilometers. Furthermore, on a sunny day, a tree can transport hundreds of gallons of water from the soil to its leaves, and apparently do it effortlessly, without making a sound and without using any moving parts... The physics that underlies water transport through plants is not exotic; rather, the application of that physics in the microfluidic wood matrix results in transport regimes operating *far outside our day-to-day experience*.[16]

Of course, trees are only possible because of an ensemble of additional elements of fitness in nature, in addition to the unique mechanism described above. These include the unique properties of the cellulose-lignin composite, which confers tensile strength and durability to tree trunks and also promotes the formation of soil.[17] Additionally, water's power of evaporative cooling (discussed earlier) protects leaves from overheating in the sun.[18] And of course trees depend on the water-retaining properties of soil (see Chapter 1).

Photosynthesis

THE END of drawing water through the soil to the roots of plants and up the trunk of a tree is to bring the life-giving properties of water and the dissolved nutrients it carries to the leaves where one of the most important chemical reactions on Earth takes place—*photosynthesis.*

In photosynthesis, light-absorbing molecules such as chlorophyll capture energy from sunlight. The chlorophyll is found in tiny organelles in leaf cells called chloroplasts. Light raises electrons in the chlorophyll to higher energy levels, and the chloroplast uses these high-energy electrons (e^-) to split water (H_2O) into hydrogen (H^+) and oxygen. The oxygen (O_2) is released into the atmosphere, and the leaf cells absorb carbon dioxide (CO_2). The chloroplast then chemically combines hydrogen and carbon dioxide to make sugars and other carbon compounds.[19]

$$CO_2 + H_2O + photons \longrightarrow (CHO) + O_2$$

carbon dioxide + water
+ light energy

carbohydrate +
oxygen

Photosynthesis is a very remarkable process, which may require exploiting the exotic process called quantum tunneling.[20]

Strictly speaking, this type of photosynthesis should be termed oxygenic photosynthesis. It is the type of photosynthesis carried out by green plants. Other types of photosynthesis utilize energy from light to synthesize organic compounds, but they do not involve the splitting of water and the release of oxygen. All advanced life forms depend on the oxygen liberated in *oxygenic photosynthesis*. And all advanced terrestrial organisms depend not just on the oxygen generated by photosynthesis, but also on the biofuels that land plants synthesize during the process.

As everyone learns at school, the energy that drives the process is derived from visible light. There is nothing contingent about this, because only electromagnetic radiation in the visual region has the right energy level for activating organic molecules for chemical reactions. Radiation in the infrared and microwave regions is less energetic than light in the visible region, and too weak to promote the necessary chemical reactions. On the other hand, radiation in the far ultraviolet (UV), gamma, and X-ray regions of the electromagnetic spectrum is *too* energetic, causing major disruptive changes—stripping electrons from atoms and molecules, ionizing them, breaking chemical bonds, and leading (for example) to mutations in DNA.[21] (Fortunately, as discussed below, our atmosphere prevents all this energetic radiation except some UV from reaching the ground.)

Although it is common knowledge that photosynthesis depends on the energy provided by visible light, it is not widely understood that visible light constitutes only an infinitesimally tiny fraction of the entire electromagnetic spectrum. As I pointed out in *Nature's Destiny*, "The wavelength of the longest type of electromagnetic radiation is unimaginably longer than the shortest by a factor of 10^{25}, or 10,000,000,000,000, 000,000,000,000. Some idea of the immensity this figure represents can

FIGURE 5.2. LEAF.

be grasped by the fact that the number of seconds since the formation of the earth, 4 billion years ago, is *only* about 10^{17}." So how much of that real estate is visible light? "If we were to build a pile of 10^{25} playing cards, we would end up with a stack stretching halfway across the observable universe," and the visual region would be "equivalent to one playing card" in that stack.[22]

Although the wavelength of electromagnetic radiation in the cosmos varies over such a colossal range, seventy percent of the electromagnetic radiation emitted from the surface of the Sun is concentrated in the exceedingly narrow radiation band extending from the near ultraviolet (0.30 microns) through the visible light range into the near infrared 1.50 microns). In other words, the Sun puts out most of its radiation in the range useful for photosynthesis.[23] And this is true of many stars in the universe, which is why the night sky is ablaze with pinpoints of visible light. *In effect, the cosmos is flooded with the "right light" fit for photosynthesis.*

The Transparency of Water

THESE CONSIDERATIONS of the immense range of EM radiations and the tiny region fit for photobiology brings us to perhaps *the* most dramatic manifestation of water's unique fitness for life discussed so far: Water strongly absorbs electromagnetic radiation in every region of the spectrum *except* for the visible region, the only region in the entire spectrum useful for photobiology. Water, in one of the most staggeringly fortuitous coincidences in all nature, lets through only the right light in an infinitesimally tiny region of the EM spectrum—the one playing card in the stack of 10^{25} stretching half way across the universe (see Figure 5.4).

Moreover, water is transparent to visible light in her three material manifestations—as liquid, gas, and ice.[24] If water or water vapor in the atmosphere absorbed visible light—the right light for photosynthesis—then photosynthesis would not be possible, and there would be no oxygen or reduced carbon fuels to sustain the metabolic activities of advanced life forms such as ourselves.

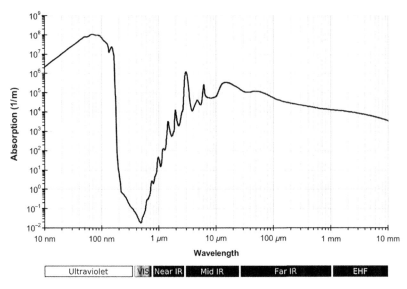

FIGURE 5.4. ABSORPTION OF EM RADIATION BY WATER. EM RADIATION < 10 NANOMETERS (X RAYS), BETWEEN 10 – 400 NANOMETERS (UV), MORE THAN 1MM (MICROWAVES).

Water not only lets through the right light, but also (as is obvious from Figure 5.4) absorbs the kind of light that life needs water to absorb—radiation from the ionizing regions (far UV) and in the mid- and far-infrared and microwave regions (the cooking regions).[25] And water vapor in the atmosphere also absorbs the wrong light in the mid- to far-infrared, microwave, and far UV regions.[26] So while water and water vapor in the atmosphere are letting through the right light for photosynthesis, they are at the same time protecting life on Earth by absorbing the wrong and damaging electromagnetic radiation on either side of the visible region.

This is a remarkable coincidence. The factors that determine that water should be transparent to electromagnetic radiation only in the tiny visible region of the spectrum are completely unrelated to those that determine that the energy levels of radiation within this tiny region are just right for photobiology. As the *Encyclopaedia Britannica* puts it, "Considering the importance of visible sunlight for all aspects of terrestrial life,

FIGURE 5.5. KRILL FEEDING ON ALGAE GROWING ON UNDER SURFACE OF SEA ICE.

one cannot help being awed by the dramatically narrow window in the atmospheric absorption... and in the absorption spectrum of water."[27]

The Transparency of Ice

As MENTIONED above, ice also lets through electromagnetic radiation in the visible band,[28] so much so that even two meters of ice is transparent to visible light.

The fact that ice is much more transparent to visible light than are the majority of solids allows for photosynthesis and oxygen production in the water under the ice. The presence of photosynthetic organisms under ice gives the undersurface of marine ice its green coloration. This anomalous property supports a rich Antarctic planktonic biota, which in turn feeds the krill, seals, penguins, and whales.

There are also elements of fitness in the very way that sea ice forms. Freezing sea ice creates, as Peter Wadham points out, "brine drainage channels" as the salt molecules are excluded from the crystal structure of the ice. Wadham points out that these have a biological role:

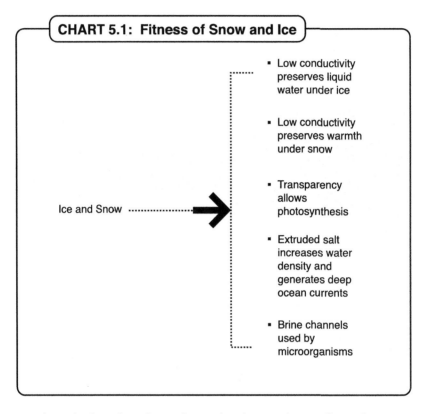

CHART 5.1: Fitness of Snow and Ice

Ice and Snow ⟶

- Low conductivity preserves liquid water under ice
- Low conductivity preserves warmth under snow
- Transparency allows photosynthesis
- Extruded salt increases water density and generates deep ocean currents
- Brine channels used by microorganisms

Phytoplankton have been observed to live on their walls, and even larger zooplankton such as amphipods have been observed to crawl up the larger channels. Within a channel there is possibly a higher light level than on the ice bottom, because of the waveguide effect of the channel for light penetrating from above, while the oscillating water flow brings nutrients and oxygen to the resident biological community. In addition the tube provides security from larger browsers.[29]

In addition to its transparency, ice possesses a surprising number of elements (some noted in previous chapters) of fitness for life on Earth. One of these, the low heat conductivity of snow and ice and its benefits to life, was well understood even two centuries ago. J. C. Loudon's *Encyclopaedia of Gardening*, published in 1824, offers these observations:

Snow and ice are bad conductors of cold; and when the ground is covered with snow, or the surface of the soil or of water is frozen, the roots or bulbs of plants beneath are protected by the congealed water from the influence of the atmosphere, the temperature of which, in northern winters, is usually very much below the freezing point; and this water becomes the first nourishment of the plant in early spring. The expansion of water during its congelation, at which time its volume increases one-twelfth, and its contraction in bulk during a thaw, tend to pulverize the soil, to separate its parts from each other, and to make it more permeable to the influence of the air.[30]

William Whewell quotes this passage in the third of the Bridgewater Treatises and adds, "In consequence of the same slowness in the conduction of heat which snow thus possesses, the arctic traveller finds his bed of snow of no intolerable coldness; the Esquimaux is sheltered from the inclemency of the season in his snow hut, and travels rapidly and agreeably over the frozen surface of the sea."[31]

Transparency and Vision

WATER'S ABSORPTION spectrum is also fit for vision, and vision is surely another biological phenomenon that is of particular relevance to advanced forms of life. Jonathan Lear starts his wonderful book *Aristotle: The Desire to Understand* with a quotation from the first lines of Aristotle's *Metaphysics*:

> All men by nature desire to know. An indication of this is the delight we take in our senses; for even apart from their usefulness they are loved for themselves; and above all others the sense of sight. For not only with a view to action, but even when we are not going to do anything, we prefer sight to almost everything else. The reason is that this, most of all the senses, makes us know and brings to light many differences between things.[32]

Aristotle was right. Vision is indeed a particularly important sense for humans. The development of technology—from making a to designing a spaceship—would be impossible without vision. Even if we concede that there might be alternative RNA life forms thriving in tiny pores in rocks, or silicon life in the dark frozen subsurface nitrogen oceans

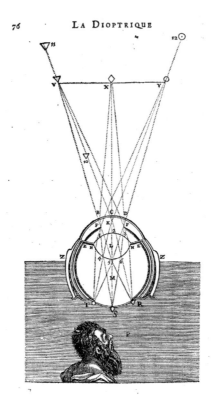

FIGURE 5.6. REFRACTION OF RAYS OF LIGHT IN THE EYE.

on Triton,[33] it is hard to imagine such life forms carrying out chemical research or building a spaceship without vision.

The same may also hold for life forms possessing vision but inhabiting a world in which the night sky and the stars are blocked out by an atmosphere impervious to light. Carl Sagan comments in *Cosmos*:

> Let us imagine that intelligent life once evolved on such a planet [Venus]. Would it then invent science? The development of science on Earth was spurred fundamentally by observations of the regularities of the stars and planets. But Venus is completely cloud-covered… nothing of the astronomical universe would be visible if you looked up into the night sky of Venus. Even the Sun would be invisible in the daytime; its light would be scattered and diffused over the whole sky—just as scuba divers see only a uniform enveloping radiance beneath the sea.[34]

The transparency of Earth's atmosphere depends of course on the properties of all the atmospheric gases, not just water vapor. But that transparency is an element of fitness in nature in which water plays a critical role.

Water and Oxygen

THERE IS another crucial element of fitness of water for photosynthesis and the manufacture of oxygen, and hence for aerobic life forms like ourselves which depend on the energy provided by oxidations (see Chapter 6). Water, as mentioned in Chapter 3, is stable in the presence of oxygen, a fact of huge significance. The unreactivity of water with oxygen is a point worth emphasizing, as many other atoms and organic molecules react strongly, often explosively, with oxygen. If water were unstable in the presence of oxygen, our advanced aerobic lifestyle would be impossible, while the many anaerobic life forms which utilize mechanisms of energy generation which do not depend on the presence of oxygen would be untroubled.

Teleological Sequence

ONE OF the more remarkable aspects of the—*mirabile dictu!*—ascent of water up the trunks of trees is the fact that the same vital fluid which is so fit to form the matrix of the cells in the leaf and enable the process of photosynthesis is the very same fluid which possesses just the right Goldilocks physical properties—tensile strength and surface tension—to raise itself from the soil to the leaf.

This is yet another case where one set of properties—water's surface tension, tensile strength, and viscosity, which raise water and its cargo of essential nutrients from the soil to the leaves—enables another set of properties—water's vital transparency to visible light, absorbance of harmful radiation, evaporative cooling (which keeps the leaf from overheating), solvation powers, and other properties which make water such an excellent matrix of the cell—to work together towards the end of photosynthesis.

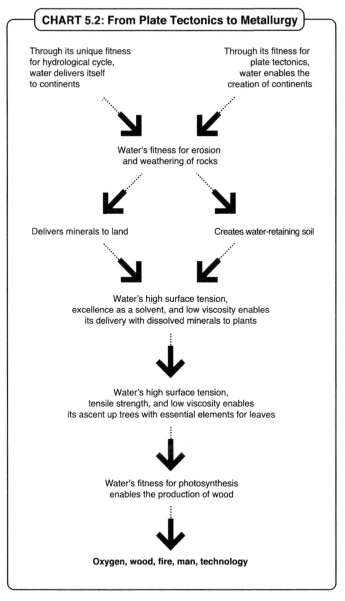

The growth of plants, the mechanism of photosynthesis, and the production of oxygen depend ultimately on an intriguing teleological series of steps, each enabled by a suite of unique properties of water. Each step in the series enables the next, a thing altogether more marvelous (*mirabile*) than the *mere* ascent of water to the top of a redwood.

If water did not have precisely the suite of properties it possesses, photosynthesis *in land plants*, and all terrestrial creatures dependent on them, would be impossible.

Earth, Fire, and Water

In this chapter we have touched on a number of additional and surprising ways in which the properties of water aid life on Earth—everything from allowing the humble pond skater to skate, through raising water through the soil and up the trunks of large trees, to enabling photosynthesis and allowing light to reach the surface of the Earth.

Most significantly, some of the elements of fitness are not generic elements of fitness for all life on Earth. Some types of extremophiles derive their energy by eating rocks and have no need for the oxygen produced by photosynthesis. They thrive in environments never graced by sunlight. But we aerobes are entirely dependent on water's fitness for photosynthesis. And not just generic photosynthesis, but the special kind that characterizes all green plants—oxygenic photosynthesis. The fitness of water for permeating the soil and climbing the trunk of a tree is necessary for *land plants*. Aquatic plants and microbes may benefit from water's transparency through photosynthesis, but they have little use for water's power to draw itself through the soil or up the small conduits in trees. Nor have aquatic plants the need for the water-retaining properties of soil.

The special fitness of water for land plants is necessary for us, too, as we are entirely dependent on land plants for the carbohydrate fuels that empower our metabolism. Without land plants, perhaps a few land animals might be able to make do on marine life, but there would be far fewer land animals, no primates, and no humans— indeed, no large macroscopic terrestrial life forms.

Moreover, oxygen and the carbon-based wood provided by trees are the two ingredients of fire. And fire itself is a terrestrial phenomenon— yet another pointer to the fact that water's fitness (and by extension) nature's fitness is not just for microbes near hydrothermal vents or for the vast inventory of marine life forms. Without water's specific fitness in so many ways and at so many steps on the path from plate tectonics to a California redwood, there would be no human-controlled fire. And without such fire, there would be no metallurgy, no modern technology. Humanity would be locked forever in a permanent, primitive stone age.

We saw in previous chapters that water, by its *own powers*, delivers itself to the land, erodes the rocks, provides the minerals for terrestrial ecosystems, rests in the soil, and transits as needed through the soil to the roots. Now we see that it is also by water's *own powers* that it raises itself and its precious cargo of minerals from the root to the leaf, enabling the production of life-giving oxygen through photosynthesis.

In all such instances, a prior element of fitness is exploited to use another element in the ensemble of fitness. It is even more marvelous when, as we have seen in this chapter, a succession of ends (each utilizing a unique element of fitness of water) are achieved by using a prior unique element or elements of fitness, making up what amounts to a teleological sequence or rational hierarchy of means to ends.

We saw earlier, in Chapter 2, that I. H. Campbell and S. R. Taylor entitled one of their papers "No water, no granite—no oceans, no continents." In the light of the topics reviewed in this and the previous chapter, we can now extend the adage: without the unique fitness of water, no granite, no oceans, no continents, no trees, no wood, no oxygen, no fire, no vision, no technology. For centuries authors have contrasted *water* with *land*, and *water* with *fire*, as polar opposites. The ancients would have been amazed by the revelation that the generation of both land and fire is dependent on the unique properties of water.

6. WATER AND HUMAN PHYSIOLOGY

[B]lood is pushed by the beat of the left ventricle and distributed through the arteries to the whole body, and back through the veins to the vena cava, and then returned to the right auricle, just as it is sent to the lungs through the pulmonary artery from the right ventricle and returned from the lungs through the pulmonary vein to the left ventricle…

This motion may be called circular in the way that Aristotle says air and rain follow the circular motion of the stars. The moist earth warmed by the sun gives off vapors, which, rising, are condensed to fall again moistening the earth. By this means things grow. So also tempests and meteors originate by a circular approach and recession of the sun.

Thus it happens in the body by the movement of the blood, all parts are fed and warmed by the more perfect, more spirituous, hotter, and, I might say, more nutritive blood… So the heart is the center of life, the sun of the Microcosm, as the sun itself might be called the heart of the world.

William Harvey, *De Motu Cordis* (1628)[1]

IN A DRAMATIC SCENE FROM A BBC DOCUMENTARY,[2] A SAN BUSH-man stands triumphant over an exhausted kudu—the largest species of antelope in Africa—readying himself to deliver a killing blow. For the previous six hours he and a handful of other members of his tribe have relentlessly chased after the kudu through the African bush, covering a distance of many kilometers during the hottest period of the day, until the kudu finally collapsed with heat exhaustion. But the San, unlike their prey, are still fit and well and their body temperatures normal. They are easily able to keep running if necessary for another few hours.

The type of hunting—persistent or endurance hunting—in which a group of humans chase a prey animal for several hours till it drops with heat exhaustion, is found not only among the Bushmen of the Kalahari but also among other tribal hunters. These include Australian aborigines, the Tarahumara of Mexico's Copper Canyon region, and the Navajo of the American Southwest.[3] It is not widely known that human endurance running speeds, ranging from 2.3 to 6.5 m/s (with easily sustainable running at 4 m/s) are fast compared to the endurance speeds of specialized quadrupedal animals. According to the authors of an essay titled "Brains, Brawn, and the Evolution of Human Endurance Running Capabilities":

> A dog of similar body mass to a human (65kg) has a trot–gallop transition speed of 3.8 m/s, and can sustain a gallop at 7.8 m/s under ideal climatic conditions for only 10–15 min… Dogs and other quadrupedal cursors cannot gallop for long periods, especially when it is hot… Thus, while a large dog can outrun a human over short distances of a kilometer or two, most fit humans can outrun any dog over longer distances.[4]

The surprising fact that humans can outrun nearly all large mammalian quadrupeds when the temperature approaches 40°C, has allowed some tribal groups to perfect the technique of persistent or endurance hunting. Significantly, all these groups live in arid tropical regions.[5]

Evaporative Cooling

BOTH THE San and the kudu are warm-blooded organisms with high metabolic rates, and both generate vast quantities of internal heat on the chase. And both are subject to a transfer of external heat to the body from the environment as the temperature of the savannah rises above 37°C. But the kudu, unable to excrete the heat generated during the chase, heat up and eventually collapse with heat exhaustion while the San are still fit and their body temperature still normal. The San's success in running down the kudu in the heat of the African sun results from many factors. Bipedal running is more energy-efficient than running on all fours, and humans can carry water with them on the chase. But more than any other factor, it is the nakedness of the human body, combined with our copious sweat glands, that maximizes the evaporative cooling effect of water on the skin. This greatly increases human heat loss compared with that of an animal (such as a kudu) with a thick furry hide that limits heat loss through evaporative cooling.

Although a kudu or a hunting dog can outpace a human over fifteen to twenty minutes, in an endurance race of ten kilometers in the heat of the day, humans can leave hunting dogs and the kudu literally for dead—thanks to our ability to exploit more fully the evaporative cooling of water.

The cooling effect of water evaporation is remarkable. As Schmidt-Nielsen points out:

> To transfer 1 g water at room temperature to water vapor at the same temperature requires 584cal… This is an amazingly large amount of heat, for when we consider that it takes 100 cal… to heat 1 g of water from the freezing to the boiling point, we see that it takes more than five times again as much heat to change the liquid water into water vapor at the same temperature.[6]

Lawrence Henderson, in his *Fitness of the Environment*, claimed that water's evaporative cooling was the highest known of any fluid,[7] and fifty years on, Arthur Needham in his *The Uniqueness of Biological Materials* could make a similar claim.[8] We now know of several substances that have a higher latent heat of evaporation, but these are mainly liquid metals at very high temperatures.[9] The evaporative cooling effect of water is still greater than any other known molecular fluid[10]—that is, a compound made up of more than one type of atom.

Although some heat is lost from the human body and from other mammals by evaporative cooling at temperatures below 30°C,[11] the evaporative cooling effect of water is most useful when ambient temperatures approach those of body temperature. This is true not only for the San on an endurance hunt but for all mammals and birds, including the kudu, that maintain body temperatures close to 37°C.[12] Mammals whose coat of fur prevents ready heat loss from the skin must lose heat by panting. This exploits the cooling potential of the large surface area of the respiratory tract, which is also highly vascularized.[13]

Besides evaporative cooling, the only other mechanisms that remove heat from the skin are radiation and conduction. But these are not of much use when the environmental temperature approaches 37°C, and are therefore of little use to the San on their hunt. Radiation and conduction, in which heat is transferred from a hot to a cold body, are significant causes of heat loss from the body surface in man and other warm-blooded homeotherms only when the environmental temperature is significantly lower than body temperature.[14] But at environmental temperatures above 37°C (normal human body temperature) conductive and radiative heat loss from the skin cease and indeed *reverse* as the body begins to soak up heat from the environment.[15]

Henderson noted over a century ago how important and effective evaporative cooling is to rid the body of excess heat as temperatures approach 37°C:

> In an animal like man, whose metabolism is very intense, heat is a most prominent excretory product, which has constantly to be eliminated in great amounts, and to this end only three important means are available: conduction, radiation, and the evaporation of water. The relative usefulness of these three methods varies with the temperature of the environment. At a low temperature there is little evaporation of water, but at body temperature or above there can be no loss of heat at all by conduction and radiation, and the whole burden is therefore thrown upon evaporation.[16]

What Henderson and many subsequent commentators do not highlight is the evident but significant fact that evaporative cooling can only serve a terrestrial organism. The evaporative cooling effect is completely irrelevant to aquatic organisms as well as to microbes living in rocks well below the Earth's surface.[17] Even aquatic mammals such as whales derive no direct adaptive use from water's high latent heat of evaporation. The cooling effect of evaporation is fit for terrestrial organisms like the San but irrelevant to whales.

Moreover, even terrestrial ectotherms (organisms such as reptiles and amphibians), which have far lower metabolic rates than mammals and generate much less body heat, make far less use of evaporative cooling. In hot conditions, they avoid overheating by sheltering from the sun.

The high latent heat of evaporation, dramatically highlighted in the success of the San in running down the kudu, reveals a fitness of water for warm-blooded terrestrial mammals and birds living in regions where temperatures are often over 30°C (most of the globe) and where they often approach 37°C (many tropical regions and deserts). But because of our relatively minimal body hair and copious sweat glands, it is arguably of more use to humans than to any other organism on Earth. That this unusual property of water is particularly useful to us is one more indicator that water is uniquely fit not just for warm-blooded terrestrial organisms, but especially for humans.

The cooling effect of evaporation is vital to us, since in humans any increase in body temperature much above 37°C is highly dangerous. If the body temperature rises over 40°C, heat stroke becomes a serious risk with potentially fatal results.

An interesting glimpse of a counterfactual world without evaporative cooling is the disease anhidrosis, an inability to sweat because of dysfunctional or non-functional sweat glands. Anhidrosis can lead to heat stroke, which may lead to premature death after strenuous exercise.[18] This tells us something. If a magic wand abolished water's high latent heat of evaporation tomorrow, millions of people in the tropical regions of the world would die within a few hours.

In short, the San and all other humans in hot climes depend on water's evaporative cooling for regulating body temperature and eliminating excess heat.[19]

Specific Heat

THE COOLING effect of evaporation is not the only thermal property of water that greatly aids temperature regulation in humans. The other is water's relatively high specific heat or heat capacity. Its specific heat capacity is not quite so dramatically anomalous as its latent heat of evaporation, but it is still higher, as mentioned in Chapter 4, than that of the great majority of familiar liquids.[20] It means, as we saw, that the temperature of a body of water changes less with the addition or subtraction of a quantity of heat than most other substances, contributing to what Tom Garrison referred to as water's "thermal inertia."[21] To cite Henderson again:

> The living organism itself is directly favored by this same property of its principle constituent, because a given quantity of heat produces as little change as possible in the temperature of its body. Man is an excellent case in point. An adult weighing 75 kilograms... when at rest produces daily about 2400 great calories, which is an amount of heat actually sufficient to raise the temperature of his body more than 32° centigrade. But if the heat capacity of his body corresponded to that of most substances, the same quantity of heat would be sufficient to raise his temperature between 100° and 150°. In these conditions the elimination of heat would become a matter of far greater difficulty, and the accurate regulation of the temperature of the interior portion of his body, especially during periods of great muscular activity, well-nigh impossible. Extreme constancy of body temperature is, of course, a matter of vital importance, at least for all highly organized beings, and it is hardly conceivable that it should be otherwise.[22]

As Henderson also points out, our metabolism has been set for maximum efficiency at a particular temperature, and it would be immensely stressed in the face of major temperature swings, especially because "an increase of 10° centigrade in temperature will more than double the rate of a chemical change."[23]

So as the Bushmen generate metabolic internal heat on the hunt and absorb external heat from their environment as the savannah heats up, the rise in body temperature is greatly buffered by the thermal inertia provided by water's high heat capacity.

The thermal inertia that comes to us compliments of water's high heat capacity clearly aids the Bushmen on their hunt, and all organisms that must maintain a constant body temperature, but if water's heat ca-

FIGURE 6.1. DIMETRODON AND EDAPHOSAURUS

pacity were significantly higher, it would pose serious problems for some organisms.

Bumblebees and dragonflies shiver to warm their thoracic flight muscles before flying on a cold morning.[24] If water's specific heat were higher, they would have to shiver longer. Indeed, a higher specific heat could pose a major physiological challenge for many ectotherms who might have trouble warming themselves on cold days. The Permian mammal-like reptile *Dimetrodon* used a large sail on its back to absorb heat and raise its body temperature. The sail could be pointed towards the sun for rapid warming, which may have allowed *Dimetrodon* to hunt before its prey became active. C. D. Bramwell and P. D. Fellgett calculate that without the sail it would take a 250-kilogram (550-pound) *Dimetrodon* approximately three and a half hours to raise its body temperature from 26° to 32°C (79° to 90°F). If the specific heat of water were double what it is, poor *Dimetrodon* may never have warmed up.[25]

An intriguing hint that the fitness of the specific heat of water might be deleterious if it were any higher is that the chosen body temperature of warm-blooded organisms is close to the temperature at which the spe-

cific heat of water is at its minimum. As the author of the London South
Bank University website notes, "The (isobaric; also called isopiestic) specific heat capacity (C_p) has a shallow minimum at about 36 °C at 100
kPa... It is interesting that this minimum is close to the body temperature of warm-blooded animals."[26]

While it is quite evident that evaporative cooling is fit primarily for
terrestrial organisms (evaporative cooling can hardly occur in the sea),
particularly those with high metabolic rates (like birds and mammals)
which generate a great deal of internal or metabolic heat and which
maintain constant body temperatures close to 37°C, it is not quite so
obvious that the high specific heat capacity of water is also of more utility for terrestrial organisms than marine. Yet this is the case, and the
reason, as we saw in Chapter 4, is that marine environments suffer far
less rapid temperature swings than terrestrial and hence marine organisms, whether warm-blooded homeotherms like whales or ectotherms
like most fishes, *have far less need for buffering against externally imposed
environmental temperature changes.*

One thing is clear: If the specific heat of water and the latent heat
and the cooling effect of evaporation were not very close to what they
are, man (and all terrestrial homeotherms that maintain a constant body
temperature in environments around the world which frequently exceed
this temperature) would be massively disadvantaged. If these properties
of water were more typical, no San would ever outrun a kudu. Indeed,
in all probability neither Bushmen nor kudu would grace the African
savannah.

Heat Conduction

SPECIFIC HEAT defends the body against rapid temperature changes, but
only radiation and heat conduction from the surface of the body (at low
temperatures) and evaporative cooling of the skin (at temperatures close
to or above body temperature) can actually rid the human body of heat.
And whichever mechanism is used to rid the body of heat, this can only
occur if the heat is transported from the body core to the skin.

One possible mechanism that might carry out the transfer is conduction. Conduction is the phenomenon (similar to diffusion) that transmits heat (vibrational energy) from molecule to molecule in some substance: gas, liquid, or solid. We experience heat conductance any time we pick up a hot piece of metal. Not all substances conduct heat equally—the range of conductivities of different materials varies over several orders of magnitude, as is the case for so many physical parameters. Air has a conductivity forty thousand times less than silver.[27] Some poor conductors—dry air, wood, etc.—are more properly termed insulators. Fluids generally have a very low conductivity of heat compared with many solids. But among common fluids water has the highest.[28]

As water is the matrix of life and makes up more than half the mass of the average human body, water is bound to be the main medium by which metabolic heat is conducted in our tissues. Water has the highest thermal conductivity of any familiar liquid—only liquid metals have higher conductivities.[29] This greatly enhances water's ability to conduct heat in the body, and is sufficient to transfer metabolic heat a distance of millimeters from the tissues to the blood in the capillaries in a relatively short period of time and to prevent a fatal buildup of heat in actively metabolizing cells. However, it is far too slow to conduct heat from the core to the periphery, a matter of meters! As we shall see below, the mass transfer of heat from the core to the periphery is not carried out by conduction but by convection—the circulation—which is only possible because of the unique fitness of water to serve as its medium.

If water's heat conductivity were much less—like that of cotton, wool, or wood—elimination of heat from the body would pose insurmountable problems, especially in situations of strenuous exercise. The tissues would boil! We would not be here, nor would any large warm-blooded multicellular organism, aquatic or terrestrial. With low heat conductance, even organisms with very low metabolic rates would eventually overheat. All chemical reactions generate some heat, and without its elimination the temperature of the tissues would rise to intolerable levels, even in the slowest metabolizing multicellular organism.

On the other hand, if the conductivity of heat by water were much greater, say like that of copper or silver, changes in the environmental temperature would be rapidly transmitted (as happens with a piece of metal) throughout the body and swamp the thermal inertia provided by water's high heat capacity. We would suffer continual massive swings in temperature.

Such a high conductance rate would be of far less concern to aquatic organisms, because temperatures in aquatic environments fluctuate far less than in terrestrial environments. The relatively low thermal conductivity of fluids, including water, compared with many other substances, is therefore an element of fitness more relevant to terrestrial organisms than to aquatic ones. Conductivity must lie somewhere close to what it is to maintain sufficient thermal stability.[30] Although the San might be advantaged by higher conductivity while on the run, because it might increase the rate of heat conduction to the skin, on a cool night they might find it impossible to maintain their body temperature at 37°C.

An intriguing aspect of the fitness of water's conductivity is mentioned at the London South Bank University website:

> For most liquids the thermal conductivity (the rate at which energy is transferred down a temperature gradient) falls with increasing temperature but this occurs only above about 130°C in liquid water... As the temperature of water is lowered, the rate at which energy is transferred is reduced to an ever-increasing extent... If our cells produce excess energy, that heat energy is transported away more efficiently at higher temperatures, so reducing its heating effect. At lower temperatures, with lower thermal conductivity, the heat is less well transported away so allowing greater heating effect. Thus our cells are more able to stabilize their temperature.[31]

Although liquid ammonia has a higher specific heat than water[32] at temperatures well below zero, and liquid sodium (at 882°C) and mercury (at 660°C) exhibit higher latent heats of vaporization than water,[33] no other liquid is known that can approach even remotely the fitness of water for heat elimination and temperature regulation in large, meta-

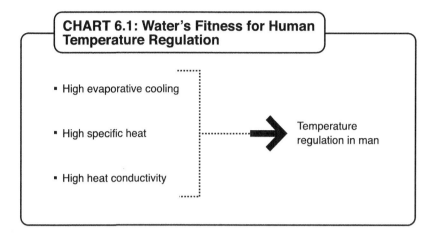

CHART 6.1: Water's Fitness for Human Temperature Regulation

- High evaporative cooling
- High specific heat
- High heat conductivity

Temperature regulation in man

bolically active, terrestrial, warm-blooded forms of life in the ambient temperature range. This is significant because 0°C to 100°C is both the approximate temperature range of life on Earth[34] and the range in which organic compounds can be most readily manipulated by biochemical systems (see next chapter).

In short, the thermal properties of water represent another set of properties that work together to serve an end, in this case to regulate body temperature in warm-blooded terrestrial organisms like man. But perhaps the most extraordinary aspect of water's fitness is that the most anomalous of water's thermal properties—its high latent heat of evaporation—is the most specifically fit for heat elimination in terrestrial organisms and especially those such as ourselves with a high metabolic rate and high generation of internal heat. If you wanted to play Plato's Demiurge and create a world for warm-blooded, carbon-based life forms—beings of our physiological design and denizens of a habitable world like planet Earth—you would need to invent water and configure her with the precise suite of thermal properties she actually possesses.

Finally, it is surely another elegant example of nature's parsimony that the very same anomalous thermal properties that are so fit for temperature homeostasis in terrestrial organisms such as humans also play a critical role in moderating the climate on a global scale, a moderation that makes the climate suitable for terrestrial life on a far greater area of the Earth's land surface than would otherwise have been the case. That these thermal properties are quite anomalous makes the parsimony and elegance of the teleology even more striking.

The Circulatory System

BECAUSE HEAT conduction in water is only efficient over short distances, this means that transporting body heat from the core to the periphery (the skin) where it can be eliminated—by radiation and conductance in lower temperatures or through the magic of water's evaporative cooling effect at higher temperatures—requires a convectional mechanism to transport the heat from the tissues to the skin.[35] This is provided by the circulatory system.

Of course the fundamental reason that all big, complex organisms require a circulatory system is not only to transport heat to the periphery for elimination but also because of a fundamental physical constraint— the inefficiency of diffusion (including heat conduction) as a transport mechanism over distances greater than a fraction of a millimeter. Diffusion rates in water are very rapid over short distances but very slow over distances of a centimeter or more.[36] The physiologist Knut Schmidt-Nielsen calculated that in the case of oxygen diffusing into the tissues, it will attain an average diffusion distance of one micron in one ten-thousandth of a second, ten microns (one cell diameter) in one hundredth of a second, one hundred microns (ten cell diameters) in one second, one millimeter in one hundred seconds, ten millimeters in three hours, and *one meter in three years.*[37]

The very great rapidity of diffusion of small molecules in water over short distances explains why unicellular micro-organisms, bacteria, protozoa, and even very small multicellular organisms can obtain nutrients and rid themselves of waste products simply by diffusion without a circulatory system. Diffusion rates in water are also fast enough over the short distances involved in intracellular metabolic processes. But the slowness of diffusion over distances of more than a few microns explains why no organism more than a few millimeters thick can acquire and dispose of

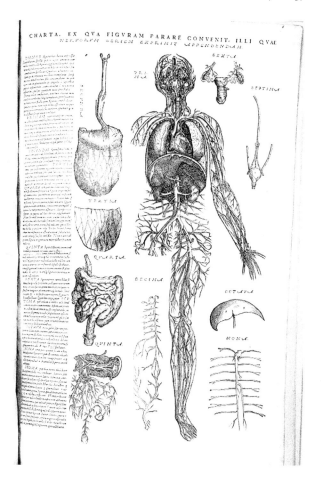

FIGURE 6.2. BLOOD VESSELS, HEART AND LUNGS. FROM ANDREAS VESALIUS,
DE FABRICA.

its metabolites (including heat) by diffusion alone. And this constraint
necessitates some sort of circulatory system.

In many simple, small multicellular organisms, the circulatory system is what is called open and the "circulation" consists of pumping
body fluids around body cavities. Insects have an open circulatory system, and oxygen is provided not via the circulation but by a series of
tiny tubes, trachea, which permeate the body tissues and even individual
cells, bringing oxygen directly to the metabolizing tissues.[38] But in all
large complex multicellular organisms—in invertebrates such as cepha-

lopods (e.g., squid, octopus) and in all vertebrates including mammals and birds—the circulatory system is closed, consisting of a vascular tree that undergoes a series of bifurcations leading from a pumping device (a heart) via increasingly smaller vessels. The system terminates in billions of tiny capillaries, generally about five microns or less in diameter (in mammals) and about one millimeter in length, which permeate the tissues of the body.[39]

The San, especially on the chase, are crucially dependent on the thermal properties of water, including the evaporative cooling of water, the high heat capacity of water, and water's ability to conduct heat generated during metabolism over short distances. But this ensemble of fitness would be of no avail without a circulatory system to take the heat from the body's core to the periphery.

Moreover, circulatory systems like our own depend on another ensemble of elements of fitness in nature. This ensemble includes a set of properties of water—many of them unusual or unique—as well as some hydrodynamic laws that must be exactly as they are or no circulatory system remotely able to sustain the life of advanced organisms would be possible.

These include: (1) the excellent solvation properties of water; (2) the incompressibility of water; (3) the relatively low density and weight of water—commensurate with the power output of biological pumps; and (4) the relatively low viscosity of water and blood (more viscous materials could not be pumped through tiny capillaries). All these fitness factors are properties of water, though other elements of fitness in nature also come into play to make possible the circulatory system, such as Laplace's Law, which relates the tension in the walls of a tube to the radius of the tube—making possible the relatively high and essential hydrostatic pressure in the capillaries.

Solvation: As the supreme solvent, water is exceptionally well fit to serve as the medium for the circulatory system. As Henderson acknowledged:

The vast utility of the solvent action of water in blood, lymph, and all the body fluids is too patent to call for comment. If, now, it can be shown that the efficiency of water is nearly or quite a maximum, as it really is, among all known solvents, then it must be evident that in another respect the fitness of water is nearly or quite maximal...

It cannot be doubted that if the vehicle of the blood were other than water, the dissolved substances would be greatly restricted in variety and in quantity, nor that such restriction must needs be accompanied by a corresponding restriction of life processes.[40]

Incompressibility: Like all liquids, water is essentially incompressible, a vital physical property of any medium which has to be pumped through the vascular tree. One can well image the problem of pumping a compressible fluid—the fluid would never leave the heart! The incompressibility of water is seldom trumpeted as a fitness characteristic, but is as essential as any other element of fitness.[41] As life can only be instantiated in a liquid (see the discussion in Chapter 7), this feature is a major piece of fortuity. Only in a microbial universe where organisms have no use for a circulatory system might the incompressibility of fluids such as water be of no consequence. But for organisms dependent on a circulatory system, water's incompressibility is crucial.

Density: Thirdly, water, like many liquids, is relatively light compared with solids such as metals or minerals. Iron is nearly eight times more dense than water and tungsten more than nineteen times more dense. The density of sulfuric acid is nearly twice that of water, and that of salt more than double. Another liquid at room temperature, mercury, is more than thirteen times the density of water. One can well imagine the difficulty of pumping blood had water been even just three times denser than it is. The five liters of blood in the average human would have weighed not five kilograms but fifteen kilograms. Probably no circulatory system would have been possible.

Viscosity: A fourth vital element of water's fitness for its role in the circulatory system is its relatively low viscosity. Water's viscosity is one of the determining factors that dictate the whole organizational design of the vascular system, and particularly the capillary beds that permeate all the tissues of the body. As mentioned in Chapter 1, the viscosity of water is one of the lowest found in fluids.[42] Only a few fluids have a viscosity much less than that of water and of those, most are only less by three to five times, while a vast inventory of fluids have viscosities many orders of magnitude greater. Water is at the lower end of the range of fluid viscosities.[43]

The pressure (P) required to pump a fluid through a pipe rises with its viscosity (V); thus, P = KV (where K is a constant; derived from the Hagen–Poiseuille equation).[44] It is therefore easy to see that if the viscosity were much increased the energy required to pump the blood through the circulatory system would be prohibitive. As things are, the head of pressure at the arterial end of a human capillary is thirty-five mm Hg, which is considerable (about one-third that of the systolic pressure in the aorta). This relatively high pressure is necessary to force the blood through the capillaries. This would have to be increased massively if the viscosity of water were several times higher, and is self-evidently impossible and incommensurate with any sort of biological pump.

As Vogel notes, powering the system consumes about ten percent of the resting energy of the body. Clearly only limited increases would be tolerated.[45] One can easily imagine the insurmountable energetic challenge if water had the viscosity of honey or treacle—several thousand times greater than water—or even of olive oil, which is about eighty times greater.

In addition to its energetic costs, increased viscosity would have other deleterious consequences. The viscosity of a fluid determines the diffusion rates of solutes in that fluid. Diffusion rates are inversely related to viscosity: V = K/D (where V is viscosity, K is a constant and D is diffusion). So the greater the viscosity, the lower the diffusion rate. As mentioned above, an oxygen molecule can traverse one hundred microns through the tissues—the thickness of ten cells in one second. But if the viscosity of water were similar to that of honey it would take an hour to cross the same distance. As things stand, if the viscosity of water were greater by a factor of ten, this would in all probability put most body cells out of diffusional reach of the nearest capillary. And redesigning the circulatory system to accommodate such a change would pose insurmountable problems.

To compensate for decreased diffusional reach due to increased viscosity, one possibility would be to increase the number of capillaries (and therefore the total volume of the blood) permeating the tissues to bring the cells back within diffusional reach. But already, as Schmidt-Nielsen points out, in the active muscles of a guinea pig there may be three thousand open capillaries per square millimeter of muscles.[46] That's equivalent to 10,000 tiny parallel tubes running down a pencil lead.[47] This is a great number, and it occupies approximately fifteen percent of the volume of the muscle. As Vogel comments, any significant increase in blood volume "would have to come at the expense of guts and gonads. Both mammals and birds invest about 6.5 percent of body volume in blood… A similar figure of 5.8 percent in octopus… argues that we are not looking at some mere accident of ancestry."[48] Across a range of very different creatures the percentage remains remarkably similar.

And of course increasing the volume of the blood would incur additional energetic costs as well.

A second hypothetical possibility to compensate for increased viscosity and decreased diffusion rates might be to keep the volume of the capillary bed as is but decrease the size of the capillaries to lessen the average distance between capillaries and tissue cells. But this option is also impractical because from the Hagen-Poiseuille equation, a fluid's rate of flow through a pipe is proportional to the fourth power of the radius of the pipe: $F = Kr^4$ (where F is the rate of flow, K a constant, and r the radius of the pipe).[49] This means that halving the diameter of a capillary would require the pumping pressure to be increased *sixteen times* to maintain the same flow.[50] And despite the low viscosity of water, capillary size could hardly be decreased further. Even if the viscosity of water were only half what it is, decreasing the size of capillaries would still require prohibitive increases in pumping power.

Simply put, if the viscosity of water were any higher, a closed circulatory system of the sort currently used by large complex life forms on Earth would not be feasible. The power needed for pumping would be prohibitive and no compensatory redesign would be possible to bring the cells within diffusional reach of the capillaries.

It is worth noting that water's low viscosity is mainly of benefit for large complex macroscopic life forms for which a circulatory system is *necessary*. As I noted in a recent paper:

> It is doubtful that many unicellular organisms would be negatively affected even if the viscosity of water were twice or three times what it is. As the temperature increases from 20°C to 100°C, the viscosity of water decreases nearly four times... so high-temperature extremophiles, for example, would still experience very rapid diffusion of metabolites, even if the viscosity of water were twice what it is. Some organisms, such as molds, can actually thrive at ambient temperatures in very viscous concentrated sugar solutions... It seems many types of unicellular life could thrive even if the viscosity of water were several times higher, but not complex metazoan organisms like ourselves.[51]

Water's low viscosity and its fitness specifically for circulatory systems in complex macroscopic life forms are yet another indication that nature's bio fitness is not merely for the generic carbon-based cell, but for beings of our physiological design.

Might water be fitter if its viscosity were lower and the diffusion rate higher? If such were the case could capillary size, blood volume, and the energetic costs of pumping be reduced somewhat? Not really. Because of the "r^4 constraint," even if the viscosity were somewhat lower, the diameter of the capillaries and the volume of the blood could be cut only by a relatively small fraction.

Additionally, there are adaptive constraints against a lower viscosity. If water were less viscous it would be less cohesive and exhibit less of what Vogel calls "groupiness."[52] Instead of exhibiting orderly laminar flow as it mostly does in the vascular tree (see Figure 6.3), it would exhibit a greater tendency to turbulence.[53] Turbulent flow may "predispose

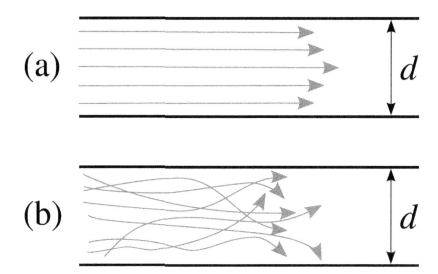

FIGURE 6.3. SHOWING LAMINAR AND TURBULENT FLOW.

to clot formation,"[54] and it has been implicated in causing damage to the endothelial lining of the arterial walls, eventually leading to atheroma.[55]

Another consequence of lowering blood viscosity and increasing turbulent flow would be an increase in the pressure required to pump the blood.[56] As Paul Clements and Carl Gwinnutt note, lowering the viscosity means the flow is "less ordered and the eddy currents react with each other, increasing drag or resistance to flow. As a result, a greater energy input is required for a given flow rate when flow is turbulent compared to when flow is laminar." The difference is substantial, such that "in turbulent flow, the flow rate is proportional to the square root of the pressure gradient, whereas in laminar flow, flow rate is directly proportional to the pressure gradient. This means that to double the flow, the pressure across the tube must be quadrupled."[57]

So ironically and counter-intuitively, if the viscosity of water were less the cost of pumping would actually be higher, at least in the larger vessels in the vascular tree, because of turbulence.[58]

Another disadvantage of turbulence is that, because the flow would be more chaotic and irregular, the relationship between the shear stress

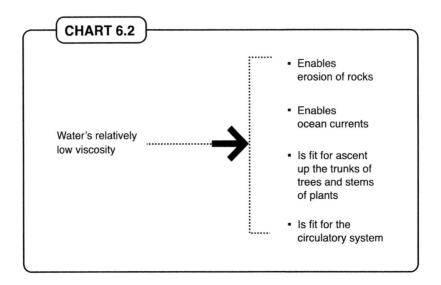

level in arterial walls and flow rates would not hold. This would make impossible the remodeling of arteries in adult life (during athletic training for example) that currently depends on sensing changing stress levels in arterial walls and maintaining a correct ratio of flow to vessel diameter.[59]

It seems likely, then, that water's fitness for a circulatory system would in all probability not be enhanced if its viscosity were much less than it is.

There are of course other constraints on the viscosity of water. Water's viscosity must be right not just for the circulation, but also to provide the right mobility for eroding rocks, to generate the ocean currents, to mix the upper layers of the ocean waters, to draw water up the stems of plants and trunks of trees, and to maintain subcellular structures. The wonder of water is that its viscosity is fit, on the one hand, to course through a capillary three microns in diameter, and on the other hand to tumble over a waterfall and replenish the mineral content of the hydrosphere.

Of Necessity

CONSIDERATION OF the various design constraints that apply to circulatory systems—energetic, volumetric, and so forth—leads to an intriguing conclusion: The only possible closed biological circulatory system is one that conforms very closely to the design actualized in all complex extant organisms on Earth (both vertebrates and invertebrates), and it requires water along with several unusual characteristics of water. The viscosity of water must be close to what it is. The density of water must be close to what it is. The rates of diffusion in water must be close to what they are. The cost of pumping must be close to what it is (a cost determined mainly by the viscosity and density of water). The proportion of volume devoted to capillaries cannot be increased (they would take up too much room) or decreased (too few capillaries would be unable to nourish the tissues). And the average diameter of the capillaries must be very close to what it is (any smaller and the cost of pumping would be prohibitive; any bigger and they would take up too much room).

Given these constraints, it is not surprising that "capillary size doesn't vary in any systematic way with body size—capillaries of elephants and whale differ little from those of bat and shrew," Vogel writes. "Nor does the value care whether red blood cells are nucleated, as in birds, or just recyclable corpuscles, as in mammals." Moreover, "Not only is the blood volume of an octopus, with its independently evolved circulatory system, similar to our own, but its capillaries are also only a little larger than ours."[60]

Given all these considerations, it is not surprising that the overall design of the cardiovascular system is so consistent across the animal kingdom, from mice to elephants. Clearly nature is fit for the circulatory system, but it's a close call. Change any one of numerous parameters—most particularly the properties of water—and no circulatory system would have been possible.

So the canonical design of the circulatory system—the entire branching manifold terminating in narrow-bore capillaries—depends on a

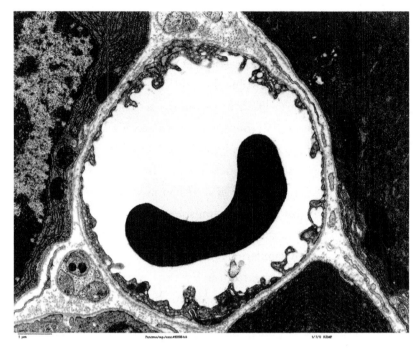

FIGURE 6.4. RED CELL IN MAMMALIAN PANCREATIC CAPILLARY.

whole set of elements of fitness in water. It is fortunate that the five-micron rule allows the passage through the capillary bed of red blood cells and leucocytes, which can squeeze through vessels of this dimension. If diffusional exchange demanded capillaries 2.5 microns in diameter or less, then no cell would ever traverse the capillary bed and no circulatory system would be feasible. Here is a genuine vital coincidence in the order of things—the size of body cells and the constraints on capillary size. And it is lucky for us not only that cells can pass through five-micron capillaries but also that the cost of reduction to five microns is commensurate with the metabolic rate and power output of biological pumps.

The impression conveyed by these considerations is that both the diameter of the capillaries and the design of the whole branching manifold are physically determined. Or, in the words of C. D. Murray, "No one can escape the impression of a physiological determinism as exemplified by the narrowness of the 'physiological range.'"[61] Given the viscosity

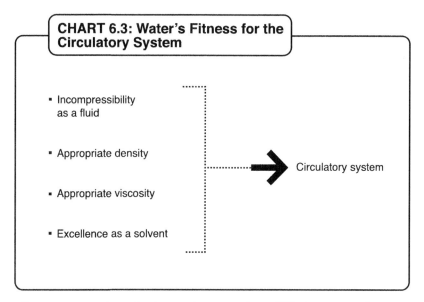

of water, energetic and volumetric constraints, diffusion rates of oxygen and other key metabolites, capillary size, and other factors not discussed here, the basic design of the whole cardiovascular system could have been predicted from first principles.[62]

In sum: Water has ideal properties to serve as the medium of the circulatory system—a vital necessity if carbon-based life is to evolve beyond the level of microbes. It is only because of this mutually fit suite of properties that our own existence as large macroscopic life forms is possible.

So, water is uniquely fitted to serve as the medium of a circulatory system, and its thermal properties are uniquely fitted for terrestrial beings—especially warm-blooded homeotherms such as ourselves. In these two suites of fitness, nature confirms her fitness for us.

Oxidative Metabolism

IN THE opening section of this chapter we reviewed the ways in which the thermal properties of water are fit for heat elimination and temperature regulation in warm-blooded terrestrial organisms. And we saw that water's most anomalous property, her uniquely high latent heat of evaporation (the highest of any molecular substance), is *only* of utility to terrestrial life forms and most specifically to terrestrial forms such as mammals and birds generating large amounts of metabolic heat, which must be excreted often at times when the environmental temperature is close to body temperature.

Here we turn to a further remarkable aspect of water's fitness for beings of our physiological design: her fitness in so many subtle and surprising ways for oxidative metabolism, the process that provides the energy we metabolically active organisms need in abundance.

It is universally agreed that complex, multicellular, carbon-based life forms are only possible because of energy released by the oxidation of reduced carbon compounds.[63] No other chemical reaction is available to biological systems that can provide metabolic energy in such abundance. We saw in the previous chapter that water is uniquely fit for the generation of oxygen via photosynthesis and specially fit for photosynthesis in large terrestrial plants. It was also mentioned that the unique stability of water in the presence of oxygen is yet another element of fitness of water for advanced carbon-based life. But unless water was *also* fit to serve as the matrix for oxidative metabolism, all her fitness for photosynthesis would be to no avail and we would not be here to contemplate its failure!

Once again, water does not disappoint.

Recall first the basic reaction of photosynthesis: Light Energy + Carbon Dioxide (CO_2) + Water (H_2O) $\rightarrow$ Glucose ($C_6H_{12}O_6$) + Oxygen (O_2). Amazingly, oxidation in the body—the very chemical reaction that utilizes the products of photosynthesis (which depends on water) is enabled to a large degree by the properties of water.

Recall, too, that the core chemical reaction of biological oxidation is the reverse of photosynthesis: Glucose ($C_6H_{12}O_6$) + Oxygen (O_2) $\rightarrow$ Carbon Dioxide (CO_2) + Water (H_2O) + Energy (ATP) + Heat. Water's fitness is immediately obvious from even a cursory consideration of how the waste products of oxidation—CO_2, heat, and water itself—are dealt with in the body.

Water herself: Although formally a waste product of oxidation, water is the matrix of life and its excretion poses minimal problems. Water is lost in the urine (a process that depends on the prior existence of the circulatory system) or by evaporation from the respiratory tract or sweat glands (in mammals), a process that depends on the capacity of water to enter readily the vapor state at body temperature. Intriguingly, some mammals actually obtain most of their water from the oxidation of the reduced carbon in their food (such as the Kangaroo rat) and have no need to take in any additional water by drinking.[64]

CO_2: Parsimoniously, it is through the properties of water that the other waste product of oxidative metabolism, CO_2, is excreted. In the body, water reacts spontaneously with CO_2 to form carbonic acid (H_2CO_3), which itself then dissociates spontaneously to generate hydrogen ions (H^+) and the bicarbonate radical (HCO_3^-): $H_2O + CO_2 -> H_2CO_3 -> H^+ + HCO_3^-$.

Both CO_2 and bicarbonate are innocuous compounds and both are soluble in water—essential fitness characteristics without which oxidative metabolism could never proceed. (And it is also fortunate that both CO_2 and bicarbonate, like water (H_2O), are fully oxidized and stable in the presence of oxygen.)

Because carbonic acid and bicarbonate result when water and CO_2 react, whatever elements of fitness they possess are indirectly thanks to water. Wherever there is CO_2 and water, there will be carbonic acid and bicarbonate. (This reaction occurs spontaneously and is rapidly accelerated in human tissues using isoforms of the enzyme carbonic anhydrase.) We saw in Chapters 1 and 3 that the end product of the water-carbon dioxide reaction, carbonic acid, helps weather rocks. Without carbonic acid, chemical weathering would be greatly slowed, so we might say water is indirectly fit for chemical weathering via the properties of carbonic acid.

As every medical student learns, most of the 200 milliliters of carbon dioxide produced per minute in an average adult human is transported in the blood mainly as bicarbonate. When the bicarbonate arrives in the lungs it is reconverted to CO_2 and H_2O where the CO_2 crosses into the alveoli and is breathed out of the body. This reaction is catalyzed by an

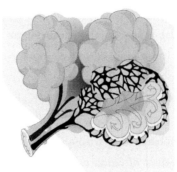

FIGURE 6.5. ALVEOLAR SACS.

enzyme, carbonic anhydrase, in the lung tissues: Hydrogen ions + bicarbonate $\rightarrow CO_2 + H_2O$.

This is widely taught, but its remarkable significance is seldom grasped. What it means is that the two waste products of oxidation in the body—water and CO_2—solve the problem of CO_2 excretion without involving any additional chemical mechanism or substances.

Thus one end product of oxidation (water), by reacting chemically with the other end product (CO_2), generates bicarbonate, which in turn is carried to the lungs by water because of water's fitness as a medium for the circulatory system. In the lungs the bicarbonate reacts with hydrogen ions to re-form CO_2, which is breathed out of the body. So the solution to the problem of CO_2 excretion resides in the properties of water and CO_2, which are themselves end products of oxidation. So water makes, dissolves, and transports bicarbonate. Water is uniquely fit chemically to generate bicarbonate by reacting with CO_2, and physically fit to transport the bicarbonate in solution in the blood to the lungs. And as we shall see in the next chapter, water also provides the proton flows used in the mitochondria to generate metabolic energy in the form of ATP.

So water, in generating and transporting bicarbonate, is profoundly fit for CO_2 excretion. This is surely one of the most parsimonious and elegant mechanisms to achieve an end in all nature. And it is utilized in every breath we take.

Heat: The third product of oxidation is heat. This too must be eliminated, since a continuous rise in body temperature would soon be fatal. And again, it is the properties of water that enable the body to keep its cool. Water's high specific heat provides a first line of defense. It is in effect water which conducts the heat from the metabolizing tissues to the blood stream. And it is water, because of its fitness to form the medium of the circulatory system, which carries the heat to the periphery where heat loss via conduction, radiation, or evaporation can occur. Heat is thereby lost from the body. Again, water is involved at every step, and each step depends on unique elements of water's fitness for life.

Another Mirabile Dictu

WATER'S REACTION with CO_2 to generate bicarbonate in the body has another benefit. Bicarbonate plays another critical role in the biology of advanced organisms such as ourselves, a role particularly important for air-breathing organisms.

To understand why this is so, first consider again the overall reaction which forms bicarbonate: H_2O + CO_2 = Carbonic acid = Hydrogen ions (acid) + Bicarbonate. This reaction is readily reversible, so whenever the level of acidity in the body rises, leading to an increase in the concentration of hydrogen ions (as occurs, for example during strenuous activity), the bicarbonate reacts with the hydrogen ions. This generates carbonic acid, which then dissociates into carbon dioxide and water. In other words, the reaction moves to the left (see figure below). Thus the bicarbonate acts as a sink for hydrogen ions, soaking them up and buffering the body against a rise in acidity. But since the reaction is readily reversible, this buffering action—the removal of the acid—can only work because the CO_2 can be continually removed from the body through the lungs (or the gills of a fish), continually drawing the reaction to the left.

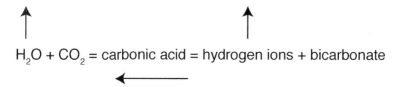

While the bicarbonate buffer defends a vast range of organisms against a rise in acid levels in body fluids, there are several intriguing features of the buffering system that are clearly fit specifically for its use as a defense against acid accumulation in air-breathing organisms.[65]

The Bicarbonate Buffer: Buffers consist of two compounds: an acid and its conjugate base. In the case of the bicarbonate buffer, the acid is carbonic acid (which is in equilibrium with the CO_2 concentration in bodily fluids) and the conjugate base is bicarbonate. When the acid level rises, the bicarbonate is converted to carbonic acid, removing hydrogen ions from the blood.

H ions + bicarbonate ⟶ carbonic acid

When the acid level falls, carbonic acid is converted to bicarbonate, releasing hydrogen ions into the blood to counteract the decrease in acidity.

H ions + bicarbonate ⟵ carbonic acid

Thus changes in the level of acid in the body are buffered.

An important feature of buffers is that the optimal pH or hydrogen ion concentration where a buffer functions most efficiently (where an acid and its conjugate base are present in equal amounts) is known as the pKa value. In the case of the bicarbonate system, the two forms are in equilibrium at about pH 6.4 in pure water and close to pH 6.1 in blood and other extracellular body fluids. But the hydrogen ion concentration in body fluids is close to pH 7. From this it would appear that the bicarbonate system is not ideally adapted to buffer the blood because it functions optimally at a pH level of 6.1, which is considerably lower than the bodily fluids' pH 7.[66]

The anomaly is only apparent, however, because the bicarbonate buffer is no ordinary buffer. As Burton Rose points out in his *Clinical Physiology of Acid-Base and Electrolyte Disorders*, calculation shows that because of the ease with which the carbon dioxide (and with it in effect the hydrogen ions) can be exhaled, the buffering capacity of the bicarbonate system is in effect increased between ten- and twentyfold (compared with an ordinary buffer), and it is far more efficient than an ordinary buffer working at its pH optimum.[67]

$$\uparrow \qquad\qquad\qquad \uparrow$$

$$H_2O + CO_2 = \text{carbonic acid} = \text{hydrogen ions} + \text{bicarbonate}$$

$$\longleftarrow$$

The Anomalous pKa Value: But there is yet another twist to this intriguing story, arising from the fact that the pKa value of the bicarbonate buffer is approximately 6.1 in the body. It turns out that this pKa value, rather than being non-ideal, is in fact perfectly suited to defending organisms from the major challenge to pH homeostasis, which nearly always comes from an accumulation of acids rather than alkalis.[68] The most familiar cause of a rise in acids in the human body is in strenuous, anaerobic exercise (such as lifting heavy weights to exhaustion or sprinting madly for a bus).

Why is this apparently anomalous pKa of the bicarbonate buffer so fit? Because it means that the organism is able to maintain a far higher concentration of bicarbonate in the blood to buffer against a rise in acid levels than would be possible if its pKa were actually seven and close to the pH level in blood.

To understand why this is so, recall that at the pH at which a buffer works with maximal efficiency, i.e., its pKa value, the concentrations of its acid and basic forms are equal. In the case of the bicarbonate system this occurs at a pH of 6.1.

pH 6.1 Bicarbonate (basic form) = Carbonic Acid (acid form)

At a pH of 7, however, the equilibrium is forced to the left and the relative concentration of bicarbonate is about twenty times greater than the concentration of carbonic acid. In the case of humans, for example, the concentration of bicarbonate in the blood is 24 mmols/L and the concentration of carbonic acid 1.2 mmols/L.

This relatively high concentration of bicarbonate is precisely what is required to protect the body from the accumulation of acids arising from the metabolism of food or anaerobic exertion. That the bicarbonate levels can be maintained at such a high level to soak up any excess acids is only possible because the pH optimum of the bicarbonate buffer is 6.1.

The Right Side of the Water: This pKa anomaly, and the buildup of bicarbonate it enables, helps all organisms protect against acid accumulation. But it most benefits air-breathing organisms like ourselves. Why? Because in an air-breathing organism the pKa anomaly inevitably leads to much higher levels of bicarbonate (up to 24 mm/L) than is possible in a water-breather using gills. This is because in the case of air-breathers like ourselves, the partial pressure of CO_2 in the lungs is many times higher than in the atmosphere (40 mm Hg compared with 0.3mm Hg in the atmosphere). And as the level of CO_2 in the lungs directly determines the CO_2 concentration in the blood, which in turn directly determines the concentration of bicarbonate in the blood, the concentration of carbonic acid is far higher than it would be if our body fluids were in direct contact with the air.

However, in the case of a poor fish, the CO_2 level in its blood is directly determined by the CO_2 level in the water in which it swims. This low level is in turn determined by the level of CO_2 in the atmosphere, which is 0.3 mm Hg, which is far, far lower than the concentration of CO_2 in the lungs of air-breathing organisms (40 mm Hg). Consequently it is impossible for a fish to maintain CO_2 and carbonic acid levels remotely close to those in an air-breathing organism such as a human. And because the ratio of carbonic acid to bicarbonate is always fixed at any particular pH (for example 20:1 at pH 7), the concentration of bicarbonate in fish blood is bound to be much less than in mammals.[69]

The high CO_2 level in the blood of air-breathing organisms, in conjunction with the anomalous pKa of the bicarbonate buffer, allows air-breathing organisms to build up a much higher bicarbonate reserve as a buffer against acid challenges.

The bicarbonate buffer system is therefore anomalous on two counts; it functions far from its hypothetical optimal pKa, and on soaking up acid it generates a neutral gas that can be readily excreted from the body. If carbon dioxide were not a gas, the buffering would be far less efficient. And if the pH optimum of the bicarbonate system were 7, the bicarbonate reserve would be far less.

Many authors have commented on the fitness of the bicarbonate buffering system for the maintenance of acid-base homeostasis. Like Henderson,[70] J. T. Edsall and J. Wyman were struck by the remarkable nature of the system: "The combination of the acidity and buffering power of H_2CO_3 [carbonic acid] with the volatility of CO_2 provides a mechanism of unrivalled efficiency for maintaining constancy of pH in systems which are constantly being supplied, as living organisms are, with acidic products of metabolism."[71]

Moreover, because of the volatility of CO_2 and the ease with which its levels in the body can be regulated by alterations in ventilation—the ease with which equation 6.4 can be pushed to the left or right—the bicarbonate buffer system provides a mechanism by which changes in ventilation in air-breathing organisms can change the level of acidity in the blood.[72]

The Solubility of Oxygen: The solubility of oxygen in water is relatively low. This fact, in conjunction with the much greater viscosity of water compared to air, greatly limits the rate at which oxygen can be extracted from water. As J. N. Maina comments:

> As a respiratory medium, air is a more cost-effective respiratory fluid: water is 50 times more viscous than air; the concentration of dissolved oxygen in water is about one-thirtieth that in air; the rate of diffusion of oxygen in water is lower by a factor of 8×10^3 compared with that in air; and the capacitance coefficient, i.e. increment of concentration per increment in partial pressure of oxygen, in water is 30 times lower in air. In saturated water, at 20°C, 1 mL of oxygen is contained in 200 g of water while 1 mL of oxygen is present in 5 mL of air (mass, 7g). All other conditions being equal, owing to the greater viscosity of water, compared with air breathing, water

breathing requires more energy to procure an equivalent amount of oxygen.[73]

The greater cost of extracting oxygen from water rules out high metabolic rates in water-breathing, carbon-based life forms. No active, warm-blooded organism extracts oxygen from water using gills, and except in science fiction scenarios, no intelligent life form in our cosmos will ever breathe through gills.

In Sum: The reaction of water with CO_2—a waste product of oxidation—to produce bicarbonate solves two basic and very different physiological problems: ridding of the body of an end product of oxidative metabolism, and maintaining acid-base homeostasis. Thus, both the problem of excreting a major end product of oxidative metabolism and the problem of acid-base balance are both elegantly solved in the properties of the same remarkable compound, water. It is a solution of breathtaking elegance and parsimony.

Is there an equivalent ensemble of fitness in all nature? As we've seen in this chapter, the two inevitable chemical end products of oxidative metabolism, water and CO_2, react together chemically to generate the bicarbonate buffer, which has ideal characteristics for buffering the body fluids of air-breathing organisms. Bicarbonate is used to transport CO_2 to the lungs. Water not only chemically reacts with CO_2 to generate HCO_3^-, but also physically transports bicarbonate to the lungs, a task dependent on the superb fitness of water to form the medium of the cir-

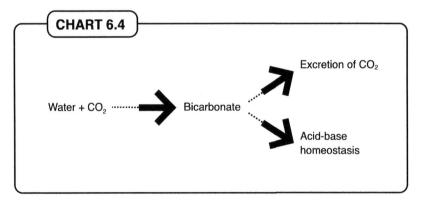

CHART 6.4

Water + CO₂ ‥‥‥⟶ Bicarbonate

Excretion of CO₂

Acid-base homeostasis

culatory system. By virtue of its high heat capacity, water soaks up excess heat (the third end product of oxidative metabolism) and transports it to the periphery, where water's high latent heat of evaporation greatly aids the excretion of heat.

Again, although the facts are not in dispute and the excretion of heat and CO_2 is in every physiology textbook, the real wonder of how the players conspire so intelligently and parsimoniously to achieve the end of heat and CO_2 excretion remains widely ignored.

Moreover, before this astonishing ensemble of fitness can be exploited, before there can be oxidative metabolism, there must be oxygenic photosynthesis to provide the oxygen and reduced-carbon fuels. And as we saw in the last chapter, water has just the right suite of properties— letting through the right light and so forth to enable photosynthesis— some of which are uniquely fit to promote photosynthesis specifically in land plants (by drawing water through the soil) and via erosion of the rocks to generate the very water-retaining properties of soil on which land plants depend (see Chapter 1).

The fact that water's fitness for photosynthesis is prior to, and necessary to exploit her fitness for, oxidative metabolism represents yet another case of a teleological sequence or hierarchy where one end A, dependent on one property or suite of properties of water X, must be satisfied prior to the serving of a second end B, which is also dependent on a suite of properties of water Y, different from those involved in serving end A. Before there can be oxidative metabolism there must be photosynthesis, and water as the matrix of life must be fit for both processes.

Destined

THE MOST widely accepted model of human origins has our species, *Homo sapiens*, coming into existence some 200,000–300,000 years ago[74] on the rich game-laden African grasslands of the late Pleistocene and from about 130,000 years ago spreading to every corner of the world.[75] Here was a new type of being—for the first time a creative agent and molder of its world. Not just a hunter, here was a story-teller, a mystic, a seer, and a dreamer. Nothing before in the history of life on Earth had hinted at the possibility of such an organism. Perhaps it is the drama of sunrise over the African savannah, perhaps the fearsome cacophony of sound as evening falls over the Ngorongoro crater, but there is something fascinating and enigmatic about the birth of mankind under African skies.

And whatever might have been the causal factors involved in our emergence, one thing we now know, as shown by the evidence reviewed in this chapter, is that our being was only possible because of the supreme fitness of nature though the properties of water for beings of our physiological design. And this implies that the fitness of nature for our biological design was prefigured into the order of nature from the beginning of time. This must count as a scientific discovery of the first order, which in itself has profound implications regarding our place in the ultimate ground of being.

Our venturing out onto that hot unforgiving savannah at the fateful moment of our birth was vitally enabled by the most anomalous of water's properties, her latent heat of evaporation, the highest of any molecular substance. Given the specific fitness of water for our *being* in so many astonishing ways, surely a knowing nature must also have prepared herself for our *becoming*? Surely our *becoming* was a matter of destiny, not chance—a matter of fate, not fortune? Surely, given water's special fitness for our being, we cannot be mere children of contingency, but rather of a deep necessity, meant to be from before the beginning of time.

And even long before our ancestors stepped out into the African sun, it was the fitness of water for plate tectonics and continental crust formation that crafted ancient Gondwana from which the continent of Africa was torn—the very land upon which our primeval ancestors first stood and first benefited from water's special fitness for beings of our physiological design. At that fateful moment of our birth, could nature have been so prepared for our being but not also for our evolutionary becoming?

7. Water and the Cell

When Szent-Györgyi called water the "matrix of life", he was echoing an old senti-
ment. Paracelsus in the 16th century said that "water was the matrix of the world
and of all its creatures." But Paracelsus's notion of a matrix—an active substance
imbued with fecund, life-giving-properties—was quite different from the picture
that, until very recently, molecular biologists have tended to hold of water's role in
the chemistry of life.

Philip Ball, "Water as an Active Constituent in Cell Biology" (2008)[1]

Water is the most important liquid for our existence and plays an essential role in
physics, chemistry, biology and geoscience. What makes water unique is not
only its importance but also the anomalous behaviour of many of its macroscopic
properties. The ability to form up to four hydrogen bonds (H-bonds), in addition
to the non-directional interactions seen in simple liquids, leads to many unusual
properties such as increased density on melting, decreased viscosity under pressure,
density maximum at 4°C, high surface tension and many more… If water would
not behave in this unusual way it is most questionable if life could have developed
on planet Earth.

Anders Nilsson and Lars G. M. Pettersson, "The Structural Origin of
Anomalous Properties of Liquid Water" (2015)[2]

THE UPPER TEMPERATURE LIMIT FOR MOST MULTICELLULAR OR-
ganisms is about 50°C.[3] This limit applies even to organisms adapted to the hot waters of hydrothermal vents, which can only survive short
periods at temperatures above 45°C.[4] The current record-holder is a species of desert ant, which can survive for short periods at temperatures
of 55°C.[5] The ant exploits its unique thermo-tolerance by foraging in
the heat of the day, in temperatures that no other animals can survive,
including potential predators.[6] Some single-celled microorganisms can
survive much higher temperatures, even over 100°C (the boiling point
of water).[7] The most thermo-tolerant microorganisms are hyperthermo-

FIGURE 7.1. STEAMBOAT GEYSER IN YELLOWSTONE NATIONAL PARK

philic species of bacteria, which can survive in temperatures of as much as 120°C. They are found in hot springs throughout the world (such as those in Yellowstone in the U.S.) and in water close to oceanic hydrothermal vents. (Water hotter than 100°C can occur in the deep ocean because the pressure is very much higher than atmospheric pressure at sea level.) The current record-holder is a methanogen discovered in the black smoker fluid of the Kairei hydrothermal field. It can survive and reproduce at 122°C.[8]

The lower limit for life is hard to determine exactly, because water (the cellular matrix of all life on Earth), freezes at 0°C. However many organisms protect themselves against freezing by cryoprotectants, and microbial metabolism has been reported down to −20°C.[9] A midge in the Himalayas survives in temperatures of −18°C.[10] At temperatures much below −20°C, however, no matter what cryoprotectants are used, freezing eventually occurs. Even if ice crystal formation is avoided, supercooled intracellular water undergoes a glass transition—vitrification—effectively causing the cessation of all metabolic processes.[11]

It seems that temperatures of about –20° to –25°C are the lower limits of life—or at least active metabolism on Earth—a limit imposed by the properties of water, the medium in which all life processes occur.[12] That being said, if metabolism could be maintained at sub-zero temperatures in some fluid other than water (ammonia comes to mind, which is liquid between –78°C and –33°C), it would be unimaginably slow.[13]

In fact, life at –40°C would be sixty-four times slower than life at 20°C. (Or more properly, the rates of chemical reaction would be sixty-four times slower.) As George Wald pointed out in a widely cited paper, at this rate the origin of life might have taken not a billion years but sixty-four billion years, or more than four times the age of the universe.[14]

Metastability

WHATEVER THE lower limit of temperature for life may be, it is likely that the highest known temperature at which bacteria can survive, 122°C, is close to the maximum possible for carbon-based life on Earth. This is because the covalent chemical bonds (ordinary electron-sharing bonds) of organic compounds become increasingly unstable as temperatures rise significantly above 100°C.

All organic compounds tend to decompose into simpler substances when subjected to minimal thermal activation. And if heated to more than 400°C in the presence of oxygen, virtually all organic compounds will undergo thermal decomposition and burn.[15] The marked thermal instability of organic compounds compared with inorganic compounds was, as Isaac Asimov pointed out, one of the lines of evidence on which early nineteenth-century chemists based the doctrine of vitalism. The other was the problem of putting Humpty Dumpty back together again, if you will—where Humpty Dumpty stands for any organic substance that has been destroyed. Writes Asimov:

> Organic materials are much more fragile and easily damaged than inorganic materials.

Water (which is inorganic) can be boiled and the resulting steam heated to a thousand degrees without damage. When the steam is cooled down, water is formed again. If olive oil (which is organic) is heated, it will smoke and burn. After that, it will no longer be olive oil.

You can heat salt (which is inorganic) till it melts and becomes red hot. Cool it again and it is still salt. If sugar (which is organic) is heated, it will give off vapors, then char and turn black. Cooling will not restore its original nature… Organic substances can be treated with heat or by other methods and converted into inorganic substances. There seemed no way, however, of starting with an inorganic substance and converting to an organic substance.[16]

In their book *The Origins of Life on the Earth*, Stanley Miller and Leslie Orgel alluded to the characteristic instability of nearly all organic compounds, especially as temperatures rise above the ambient range.[17] The amino acid alanine, for example, has a half-life of twenty billion years at 0°C, of only three billion years at 25°C, and of only ten years at 150°C, a decrease of more than a billion-fold. And alanine is not exceptional.[18]

Recent studies on the thermal stability of organic compounds, including one published in *Nature*,[19] reported that at 250°C many of the key organic compounds used by living things decompose at rates too fast to measure, or have half-lives of the order of minutes or seconds.[20] These include such important compounds as amino acids (the building blocks of proteins), nucleotide bases (the building blocks of DNA and RNA), and the energy-rich compound adenosine triphosphate (ATP), which plays a vital role in the energy metabolism of all living cells on Earth.

The contrast between the stability of the bonds that bind the atoms in inorganic compounds with the relative instability of the bonds in organics is easily demonstrated by a simple experiment.

Take three spoons. Fill one with sand, the second with salt (NaCl, in which the two inorganic substances, sodium and chlorine, are linked by ionic bonds), and the third with a particular sugar ($C_{12}H_{22}O_{11}$, in which the atoms are linked by covalent bonds between carbon, hydrogen and oxygen). Now heat all three spoons over a candle flame. After a short while, when the temperature reaches 186°C, the sugar bubbles and boils and appears to melt (actually it is decomposing), turning into a yellow fluid consisting of glucose ($C_6H_{12}O_6$) and fructose ($C_6H_{12}O_6$), which on further heating darken into a viscous fluid, consisting of caramelan ($C_{12}H_{18}O_9$), caramelen ($C_{36}H_{50}O_{25}$) and caramelin (average molecular formula $C_{125}H_{188}O_{80}$).[21] On drying the mix turns into a brittle solid, toffee. If the heating is continued after a while the "toffee" is burnt to CO_2 and H_2O and all that is left is a black film of carbon on the surface of the spoon. Altogether a dramatic set of changes to one organic compound on heating! Yet while these chemical transformations are occurring in the sugar, the sand and the salt remain completely unchanged.

Many other examples could be alluded to which indicate the instability of organic chemicals and their tendency to decompose on heating. Lawrence Henderson noted this instability, but he recognized that it was in fact an element of fitness, one that made possible the universe of complex and diverse organic compounds:

> Not less valuable to the organism than the multiplicity of organic substances… are the great variety of chemical changes which they can undergo, and that characteristic instability which renders such great complexity of chemical behaviour easily attainable.[22]

J. B. S. Haldane[23] and Arthur Needham emphasized the same point. They characterized organic (carbon) compounds as "metastable" or marginally stable in ambient conditions, and thus easily able to undergo chemical transformations. As Needham comments, "Carbon seems to have the best of both worlds, in fact, combining stability with lability, momentum with inertia… The heat of formation of carbon compounds from their immediate precursors is rarely very great, so that, once the initial steps of carbon dioxide reduction have been effected, a large variety of compounds form relatively spontaneously."[24]

It is precisely because of their characteristic metastability, and the relatively low energy levels of the bonds that bind their atoms together, that organic compounds can be manipulated by biological systems.

There is another type of bond in living systems, quite different from ordinary electron-sharing covalent bonds: the so called "non-covalent" or "weak bonds." These are the bonds that fold the key macromolecules of life, such as proteins and nucleic acids, into their native 3-D shapes. They include hydrogen bonds and van der Waals forces. They are far weaker than covalent bonds and more susceptible to disruption on heating.[25] This occurs in the slow cooking of meat at 85–90°C. The gentle heating causes the familiar softening of the meat, but it does not break the covalent bonds in the organic compounds that make up the meat. The softening is due to the breakage of the weak bonds that hold proteins in their native 3-D shapes, causing their unravelling and denaturation. But again, this vulnerability is a strength, for it is the very weak-but-not-too-weak nature of these bonds that allows the key macromolecules of life, including proteins and nucleic acids, to perform their extraordinary gymnastics that make them so fit to perform the various roles they play in the cell.

The Need for a Liquid Matrix

THERE IS almost universal agreement that a complex living system remotely comparable with cellular carbon-based life on Earth could only be instantiated in a liquid medium.[26] The other two states of matter, solid and gaseous, seem to be excluded on fundamental grounds. In crystalline solids (with atoms held in regular arrays) and glassy solids (with atoms irregularly packed), the atoms are in rigid contact with one another and there is very little scope for the dynamic molecular processes associated with life. Gases, on the other hand, are far too changeable and unstable to be seriously considered as candidates for the matrix of life. As Needham comments:

> Only systems based on a fluid [i.e., liquid] medium could display the properties which we should accept as Life. Gaseous systems are too volatile and lack the powers of spontaneously segregating subsystems... At the other extreme solids are too rigid and inert... In gases... the tendency towards a uniform distribution of energy, is very rapid but in liquids is slow enough for local differences to be

maintained by a modest inflow and for steady states to be set up. All gases mix freely with any other, but not all liquids. Some form discontinuities or interfaces, with solid-state properties, where they meet another liquid, and complex polyphasic systems are readily formed… which further… increase the potentialities for steady-state perpetuation.[27]

We are all familiar with clouds, which are nebulous masses of tiny liquid droplets, or in more scientific terms, segregations of liquid-in-gas colloids. But as Needham points out, clouds are a rare exception to the general rule that segregating subsystems are unusual in a gas. And the very transience of cloud patterns graphically illustrates the unsuitability of gas as a medium for stable segregating subsystems.

The Prime Coincidence

THE INSTABILITY of organic compounds above ambient temperatures means that they can probably be exploited by living systems only at temperatures up to 122°C. It is only below this temperature that the majority of carbon compounds exhibit the right metastability (lability and stability) to permit the intricate and sophisticated manipulation of their constituent atoms by the chemical machinery of life. At temperatures below 0°C, reaction times become much slower. It is probably safe to say that carbon-based biochemistry as it exists in living cells on Earth is only possible within a temperature range of (to be generous) –50°C to 130°C. Although this 180°C temperature range (between –50°C and 130°C) may appear large from our perspective, it represents an unimaginably tiny fraction of the total range of all temperatures in the cosmos. The temperature of the universe shortly after the Big Bang is thought to have been 10^{32}°C (ten followed by thirty-one zeros).[28] Current temperatures range from –279°C (very close to absolute zero) to several thousand million degrees inside some of the hottest stars.[29] Even inside our own sun, which is not a particularly hot star, the temperature is of the order of fifteen million degrees,[30] and its surface temperature is 6,000°C.[31]

So the right temperature range for biochemistry is an inconceivably small fraction—about 10^{-29}—of the total temperature range in the cos-

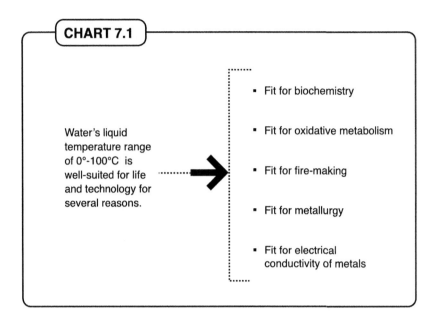

CHART 7.1

Water's liquid temperature range of 0°-100°C is well-suited for life and technology for several reasons.

- Fit for biochemistry
- Fit for oxidative metabolism
- Fit for fire-making
- Fit for metallurgy
- Fit for electrical conductivity of metals

mos. This situation is similar to that of viscosity: the viscosity of water occupies a minute fraction of the range of viscosities of liquids and solids—about 10^{-25}.[32]

So life requires a liquid matrix. And as we have seen, the optimal matrix is water, which just happens to be liquid in the temperature range required for the metastability of organic compounds uniquely fit to serve as the building blocks of life. This is surely an arresting concurrence! Despite its fitness for the hydrological cycle, for tectonic recycling, for global homeostasis and the climate machine, for the ocean current conveyor belt, for temperature control in warm-blooded animals, for tall trees, for circulation of the blood, if this additional concurrence did not hold—if water were not a liquid between 0°C and 100°C—water would not be fit for life. All these other elements of fitness would be of no avail; almost certainly there would be no carbon-based life in the cosmos.

Curiously, within the same temperature range nature is fit for many other vital aspects of life on earth. At temperatures below 50°C, the current atmospheric level of oxygen (twenty-one percent) both supports human respiration and makes fire relatively controllable. So humans were able to tame fire, making metallurgy possible and taking the first key step on the route to modern technology—including electronic technology (see my *Fire-Maker* monograph for details and references). In the temperature range between 0°C and 50°C, oxygen is also most soluble in water.[33] Aerobic marine organisms obviously need dissolved oxygen, but so do aerobic terrestrial organisms, because oxygen must first dissolve in blood before it can be combined with hemoglobin for transport to the tissues. So the temperature interval in which water is a liquid is ideally fit for biochemistry, for aerobic organisms, for making fire, and for utilizing metals for technology.

Given the range of temperature in the cosmos, how fortuitous that so many elements of fitness are compressed in this tiny temperature range, only $1/10^{29}$ of the total range of cosmic temperatures.

Why Water is Weird

As we have seen, many of the anomalous properties of water that make it uniquely fit for life reside in its hydrogen-bonded network. This network is the reason that water exists as a liquid on Earth between 0°C and 100°C, and can exist in the three states of matter in ambient temperatures between –90°C (Antarctica) and 50°C (Sahara). The network provides the cohesiveness responsible for raising water's melting temperature and boiling temperature to far higher levels than is the case for other comparable light molecular substances.

Briefly and leaving out many details: Water molecules possess a V-shaped structure (see diagram, where the dark balls are oxygen atoms at the base of the V and the small white balls are hydrogen atoms).

The molecules form hydrogen bonds with neighboring molecules; each oxygen atom, which is negatively charged, forms two hydrogen bonds with hydrogen atoms on neighboring water molecules. As can be seen in the diagram, this causes the formation of a network that extends right through the water. This network confers a unique stickiness or cohesiveness to water that holds the molecules together and raises the

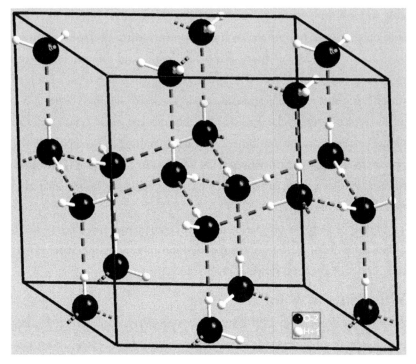

FIGURE 7.2. HYDROGEN BONDS IN WATER.

melting and boiling points. No other fluid possesses the same degree of cohesiveness.

Key to this is that each water molecule has up to four bonds. (Hydrogen fluoride and ammonia each can only form two.) The resulting sturdiness lends water its higher viscosity, melting point, and boiling point. But for these intermolecular attractive forces provided by the hydrogen-bond network, as Needham points out, water "would be gaseous at the Earth's surface temperatures."[34] Water's existence in the three basic states of liquid, solid, and gas in ambient conditions (discussed in Chapter 1) would not be possible. As Alok Jha comments:

> Given that water molecules are made from two such light atoms, the textbook rules of chemistry say that our planet should have no liquid oceans. All of the water on our planet should rightly exist as a vapor, part of a thick muggy atmosphere that sits above a bone dry surface.[35]

And again, the existence of water as a liquid in the ambient temperature range on Earth is one of the grand coincidences in nature. For it is only in the ambient temperature range that organic compounds are metastable and readily manipulated by biochemical systems.

At the same time, although ambient temperatures are well below water's boiling point, a significant amount of water enters the atmosphere as a gas (water vapor) at temperatures above 0°C. At 30°C, for example, air saturated with water vapor may contain thirty grams of water per cubic meter.[36] And because in the higher latitudes and at high elevations the temperature is often below 0°C (in some places such as Antarctica permanently far below zero), water also exists as a solid (ice). It is only because of its anomalously high melting and boiling points that the three material states of water can exist in ambient conditions on Earth, and hence the hydrological cycle depends on water's uniquely cohesive hydrogen-bonded network.

This cohesive network is not only responsible for the anomalous existence of liquid water on Earth and for the hydrological cycle; it is responsible for many of the anomalous properties of water that are fit for life in different ways. The London South Bank University website lists seventy-three anomalous properties of water,[37] and of these, about thirteen or more are of great utility for life on Earth. These properties include (1) its high dielectric constant and great solvation powers, particularly for charged or polar compounds, (2) its decreased density on freezing, (3) its maximum density at 4°C for fresh water, (4) its maximum density at −1.8°C for sea water, (5) its high heat capacity, (6) its high latent heat of vaporization, (7) its high latent heat of freezing, (8) its high surface tension, (9) its hydrophobic force (the tendency to clump together nonpolar substances or parts of molecules), (10) its low but not exceptionally low viscosity, (11) its capacity for proton flow or making "water wires," and (12) its relatively high (for a liquid) conductivity of heat. Many of these anomalous properties have been discussed by Henderson, Edsall, and Needham, and more recently by Ball.[38] Many of them can be explained by the existence of water's hydrogen-bond network.

True, water is still one of the least understood of all liquids, and just how this network contributes to some of these unique properties remains controversial.[39] Yet whatever their ultimate cause or explanation may prove to be, these anomalous properties are an empirical reality, and clearly fit for life on Earth.

The Alkahest Again

CARBON-BASED LIFE—LIFE on Earth—needs a matrix that is fluid in the ambient temperature range so the cell can easily manipulate its biochemical components. But other criteria must be satisfied if a fluid is to form the matrix of life, a medium in which biochemistry can be carried out. Above all, the fluid needs to be a good solvent, able to carry in solution the vast range of ions and chemicals necessary for the cell to function. And water wonderfully fits the bill.

As a solvent, water is incomparable. Alok Jha comments:

Liquid water is such a good solvent, in fact, that it is almost impossible to find naturally occurring pure samples and even producing it in the rarefied environment of the laboratory is difficult. Almost every known chemical compound will dissolve in water to a small (but detectable) extent. Related to this, because it will interact with everything, over long periods of time water is one of the most reactive and corrosive chemicals we know.[40]

The late Felix Franks, perhaps the leading modern authority on water, echoed this sentiment.[41] Water is indeed the *Alkahest*. The near-universal solvent the alchemists sought was right under their noses all along.[42] No other liquid comes close. Lawrence Henderson comments:

As a solvent there is literally nothing to compare with water... the solubility in water of acids, bases and salts, the most familiar classes of inorganic substances, is almost universal.[43]

Virtually all organic substances that either carry an ionic charge or contain polar regions—which includes the great majority of all organic compounds in the cell—dissolve readily in water. Many different kinds of polar compounds are dissolved (along with ions) in the water of such biological fluids as blood, the sap of plants, and the cytosol within all

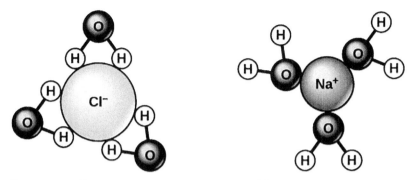

<small>FIGURE 7.3. SHOWING HYDRATION SHELLS. MODIFIED FROM IMAGE BY OPENSTAX COLLEGE, BIOLOGY. [CC BY 4.0 (HTTPS://creativecommons.org/licenses/by/4.0/)] via khanacademy.org.</small>

cells. Even large molecules such as proteins can dissolve in water if they have ionic or polar regions on their surface. The only polar (or charged) molecules which do not dissolve are very large molecules like cotton or cellulose.

Because of its polarity, a water molecule can form electrostatic interactions (charge-based attractions) with other polar molecules and ions. The negatively charged oxygen atoms form bonds with positively charged ions such as sodium (Na+), while the positively charged hydrogen atoms form bonds with negatively charged ions such as chloride (Cl-). Since there are nearly always many water molecules relative to solute molecules, these interactions lead to the formation of a three-dimensional sphere of water molecules, or *hydration shell*, around the solute. Hydration shells allow particles to be dispersed (spread out) evenly in water. This keeps the charged solutes apart and unable to combine and precipitate out of solution.[44]

As Ball writes:

> Water is an extremely good solvent for ions. In part, this is the result of water's high dielectric constant, which screens the ions' Coulombic potential effectively and prevents the aggregation and crystallization of ions of opposite charge. By the same token, water is an efficient solvent for biomolecular polyelectrolytes such as DNA and proteins, shielding nearby charges on the backbone from one another.[45]

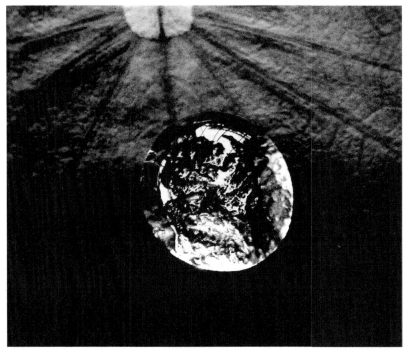

FIGURE 7.4. DROP OF WATER ON LEAF ILLUSTRATING THE HYDROPHOBIC
FORCE.

The Hydrophobic Force

THERE is one exception to the solvation powers of water, one that promotes rather than undermines its fitness for life. It is common knowledge that oil and water don't mix. If you pour oil on water, it will form
a separate layer on the surface. Oils consist of long hydrocarbon chains
that don't dissolve in water because the electrons are equally distributed
over the carbon and hydrogen atoms. So there are no positively charged
or negatively charged regions in the chain.[46]

Since hydrocarbon chains cannot disrupt the hydrogen-bonded network of water, oil molecules are forced to associate together in water-
excluded "hydrophobic" clumps or layers. (Ionic or polar molecules are
"hydrophilic," and molecules with both polar and non-polar regions are
said to be "amphiphilic.") The hydrophobic effect explains the separation
of a mixture of oil and water into its two components, and the beading

of water on nonpolar surfaces such as waxy leaves (see figure). And this is crucial to several important biological processes. As Ball comments:

> Hydrophobic solutes in water experience a force that causes them to aggregate. This hydrophobic interaction is responsible for several important biological processes... for the aggregation of amphiphilic lipids into bilayers, with their hydrophobic tails "hidden" from water and their hydrophilic heads at the surface, for the burial of hydrophobic residues in polypeptide chains that helps proteins to fold and to retain their compact forms, and for the aggregation of protein subunits into multi-subunit quaternary structures. There is a tendency for even rather small hydrophobic moieties to cluster— something of the sort seems to happen for methanol dissolved in water, leading to dynamic heterogeneity of the mixture.[47]

So instead of being a flaw in the supreme solvent, the hydrophobic effect is one of the most important elements of water's fitness for life, in particular at the cellular level. The hydrophobic effect helps to drive protein folding, because it forces amino acids to clump together in the center of the proteins. According to Charles Tanford, "the hydrophobic force is the *energetically* dominant force for containment, adhesion etc., in all life processes. This means that the *entire* nature of life as we know it is a slave to the hydrogen-bonded structure of liquid water" [emphasis in original].[48] And by forcing the non-polar chains of lipids to associate in the middle of lipid bilayers, the hydrophobic effect forms biological membranes. Water may be the universal solvent, but its inability to dissolve uncharged molecules—its hydrophobic "flaw"—is almost as important as its power to dissolve polar compounds. Water is thus a potent organizer of the higher architecture of living cells.

On a historical note, it is interesting that as science has progressed more and more elements of fitness of water for life on Earth have been uncovered. In *The Fitness of the Environment*, Lawrence Henderson never mentioned the hydrophobic force because its importance for life (specifically, its role in folding proteins into their natural conformations and in ordering the lipid bilayer cell membrane) was not understood.

Viscosity

As ALREADY mentioned in Chapter 1, like many physical parameters the viscosity of solids, liquids, and gases varies over more than twenty orders of magnitude. This is a vast range, and within this immensity, the viscosity of water has to be within an order of magnitude of what it is in order to serve a number of ends: forming the medium of the circulatory system, eroding the rocks, generating ocean currents, and of course, forming the matrix of the cell.

If the viscosity were much lower than it is—approaching the viscosity of a gas—the cell's delicate cyto-architecture would be subject to continual and much more intense Brownian bombardment (particle mobility in a fluid is inversely related to viscosity) and far less stable.[49] It is doubtful if anything remotely resembling the canonical cell would be feasible. In short the viscosity of water could hardly be much lower!

But it is equally hard to see how the viscosity of water could be much higher than it is and still serve as the matrix of the cell. We saw in the previous chapter that diffusional constraints play a major role in determining the configuration of the vascular system, including, for example, capillary size and distribution. Diffusional constraints also play a critical role in the design of the cell. Many cells are approximately ten to twenty microns in diameter, and this is determined largely by diffusional constraints.[50] Because diffusion is inversely related to viscosity, even though active transport and facilitated diffusion mechanisms do play an important role in shifting metabolites and ions into and around the cell, passive diffusion is still of universal utility, and increased viscosity would impose severe constraints on cellular size and metabolism.

And it is not just diffusional constraints that increased viscosity would impose on cells. The controlled movement of large macromolecules and small organelles would be impossible, as would processes like cell division. All the vital activities of the cell would be effectively frozen and any sort of remotely recognizable cellular life would be impossible. The development of higher organisms, which depends on the ability of cells to move and crawl around during embryogenesis, would certainly be impossible. So would the circulatory system in higher organisms. No organism would move in water, whether a bacterium or a fish. Self-evidently, the viscosity of water would not be fit for life in any way we can imagine if the viscosity were much more than ten times higher.[51]

Although it is not possible to determine precisely how narrow the range of viscosities/diffusion rates compatible with the canonical cell might be, all the evidence suggests that it could not be much higher or lower and that the viscosity of water is another element of water's fitness for the cell: not too low, not too high—just right!

Proton Wires

The hydrogen-bonded network is also critical for generating cellular energy—it provides "water wires," long chains of linked water molecules for moving protons around in the cell. As Alok Jha points out, while other charged particles involved in cellular functions have to move themselves physically from one place to another, "protons can pass their energy along a hydrogen-bonded water wire without moving themselves at all, thanks to the so-called Grotthuss mechanism." Jha continues:

> A proton can become attached to one end of the water wire and, within a fraction of a second each of the hydrogen bonds further along the length of the wire spin around in sequence so that a proton drops off the water molecule at the other end of the wire. The initial proton has not moved any further than the starting end of the wire but its charge and energy have been conducted along the wire's length."[52]

This unique mechanism, dependent on water's unique hydrogen-bonded structure, is exploited by all living things to generate cellular energy. As Nick Lane puts it:

> Essentially all living cells power themselves through the flow of protons (positively charged hydrogen atoms) in what amounts to a kind of electricity—proticity—with protons in place of electrons. The energy we gain from burning food in respiration is used to pump protons across a membrane, forming a reservoir on one side of the

membrane. The flow of protons back from this reservoir can be used to power work in the same way as a turbine in a hydroelectric dam. The use of cross-membrane proton gradients to power cells was utterly unanticipated. First proposed in 1961 and developed over the ensuing three decades by one of the most original scientists of the twentieth century, Peter Mitchell, this conception has been called the most counterintuitive idea in biology since Darwin, and the only one that compares with the ideas of Einstein, Heisenberg and Schrödinger in physics... We also know that the use of proton gradients is universal across life on earth—proton power is as much an integral part of all life as the universal genetic code.[53]

It's fascinating that the use of proton flows across membranes to generate energy is dependent on two unique properties of water, the hydrophobic force that assembles membranes and the proton flow across those same membranes. Only water can assemble the membranes and only water can provide the wires. Thus water is fit in two crucial ways for bioenergetics.

Biophysicist Harold Morowitz has specifically alluded to the unique fitness of the wires for bioenergetics:

> The past few years have witnessed the developing study of a newly understood property of water [i.e. proton conductance] that appears to be almost unique to that substance, is a key element in biological-energy transfer, and was almost certainly of importance to the origin of life... The more we learn the more impressed some of us become with nature's fitness in a very precise sense... Proton conductance has become a subject of central interest in biochemistry because of its role in photosynthesis and oxidative phosphorylation.[54]

As Morowitz explains, both of these key processes use proton conductance and hydrated ions, which are major features of water: "Once again the fitness enters in, in the detailed way in which the molecular properties of water are matched to the molecular mechanisms of bio energetics."

It is again because of the hydrogen-bonded network that water is a good conductor of protons.

The Active Matrix

WATER IS fit for cellular physiology and biochemistry for many reasons: it remains a fluid in the ambient temperature range, it has great solvation powers for all charged and polar compounds, its viscosity is right, and so forth. But water is far more than just a passive matrix. Water plays so many well-understood key roles in active processes, such as folding proteins, assembling cell membranes, and providing proton flows (especially proton flows in which water is clearly a key player if not *the* key player in bioenergetics), that it is already clear that it is indeed the active player in cellular physiology that Szent-Györgyi envisaged when he said, "Life is water, dancing to the tune of solids."[55]

Philip Ball concurs. "It has become increasingly clear over the past 2 decades or so that water is not simply 'life's solvent' but is indeed a matrix more akin to the one Paracelsus envisaged: a substance that actively engages and interacts with biomolecules in complex, subtle, and essential ways," he writes.[56] Concerning water's active participation in the life of the cell, Ball comments:

> It is often overlooked that the famous double-helical structure of DNA is not intrinsic to that molecule but relies on a subtle balance of energy contributions present in aqueous solution. Without water to screen the electrostatic repulsions between phosphate groups, the classic, orderly helix is no longer viable. Thus, DNA undergoes conformational transitions, and even loses its double helix, in some apolar solvents… and even though both experiments… and MD [molecular dynamic] simulations… suggest that the double helix is not lost entirely in the gas phase, it has none of the elegance and order familiar from DNA's iconic representations.[57]

Ball concludes by describing various roles water plays in a host of biochemical processes:

> It maintains macromolecular structure and mediates molecular recognition, it activates and modulates protein dynamics, it provides a switchable communication channel across membranes and between the inside and outside of proteins. Many of these properties do seem to depend, to a greater or lesser degree, on the 'special' attributes of

the H_2O molecule, in particular its ability to engage in directional, weak bonding in a way that allows for reorientation and reconfiguration of discrete and identifiable three-dimensional structures. Thus, although it seems entirely likely that *some* of water's functions in biology are those of a generic polar solvent rather than being unique to water itself, it is very hard to imagine any other solvent that could fulfill all of its roles—or even all of those that help to distinguish a generic polypeptide chain from a fully functioning protein. The fact that fully folded proteins moved from an aqueous to a nonaqueous environment may retain some of their functionality does not alter this and does not detract from the centrality of water for life on earth... it is not sufficient, in this context, to imagine a clear separation between the "molecular machinery" and the solvent. There is a two-way exchange of behaviors between them, and this literally erases any dividing line between the 'biological components' and their environment.[58]

In the recent book *Water and the Cell*, editor Gerald Pollack writes that "water within cells is to a major extent ordered differently than bulk water, and functions not as an inert solvent, but as an active player... Understanding water order in biological systems is key to an understanding of life processes."[59] Even just some of the book's chapter titles drive home how important water's active role may be for cellular physiology. These include "Information Exchange within Cellular Water" and "Some Properties of Interfacial Water: Determinants for Cell Architecture and Function."

Further Revelations

GIVEN THE many ways water is fit for life on Earth, and given that scientific advances over the past two centuries have uncovered more and more ways water is uniquely fitted for life, it seems likely this trend will continue. And one area especially likely to reveal many more elements of fitness is water within the cell. It is a remarkable fact that despite its known importance, and massive research efforts devoted to it, the structure of intracellular water is still less understood than the geophysics of

Mars or the chemistry of hydrothermal vents. It is currently the subject of considerable debate.

Further knowledge of intracellular water could well reveal that cell water is indeed very much more than a passive matrix (although even as passive matrix its fitness is profound). Several authors, including Gerald Pollack and Gilbert Ling, have argued that it is organized in ways that differ radically from bulk water, including being ordered into layers that extend considerable distances from intracellular interfaces.[60] Pollack has also argued, as Philip Ball notes, "that the cytoplasm is like a gel (without the macromolecular network that makes ordinary gels cohere), which maintains its integrity if relatively large sections of the cell membrane are removed."[61]

In his book *Cells, Gels, and the Engines of Life*, Pollack cites the difficulty of dehydrating wood, and the survival of cells in extreme subzero temperatures without ice crystal formation, as evidence of the complex, higher-order structure of cell water.[62] If cell water is really ordered very differently from bulk water, there is good reason to believe that these novel structures might possess additional elements of water's unique fitness for cellular functions. Given the known fitness of water in almost every conceivable way for life on Earth, it would not be surprising if water's fitness for biochemistry and the workings of the canonical cell turn out to be far more profound than currently understood.

8. CONCLUSION

In a universe whose size is beyond human imagining, where our world floats like a dust mote in the void of night, men have grown inconceivably lonely. We scan the time scale and the mechanisms of life itself for portents and signs of the invisible. As the only thinking mammals on the planet—perhaps the only thinking animals in the entire sidereal universe—the burden of consciousness has grown heavy upon us. We watch the stars, but the signs are uncertain. We uncover the bones of the past and seek for our origins. There is a path there, but it appears to wander. The vagaries of the road may have a meaning, however; it is thus we torture ourselves.
Loren Eiseley, *The Immense Journey* (1946)[1]

To see a World in a Grain of Sand
And a Heaven in a Wild Flower
Hold Infinity in the palm of your hand
And Eternity in an hour
William Blake, "Auguries of Innocence" (1803)[2]

IS THERE A TALE LIKE THE TALE OF WATER? CAN ONE CONCEIVE OF A substance as profoundly purposeful, serving such a diversity of vital ends? Has any substance remotely like water been described even in the most *outré* annals of science fiction? Who might have guessed or imagined in even the most unrestrained flight of fancy that in this simple substance, one of the simplest of nature's creations, composed of only three atoms—two of hydrogen and one of oxygen—and only a ten-millionth of a millimeter across, there would be so much design?

There are more ends served in these three magic atoms than in any other natural form, and far, far more, and far more marvelous, than in any artifact *created by or conceived of by man*. No words can express the wonder of such manifold purpose, so many vital ends, compressed in such a tiny piece of matter. Water is the matrix of the cell, the blood of the Earth, the maker of mountains, the sustainer of life.

And given that hydrogen and oxygen are two of the three most abundant elements in the cosmos, it seems that nature was focused from the beginning on making water, and through its unique magic the phenomenon of life in the universe. If there is a path, as Loren Eiseley surmised, if the "vagaries of the road" do have a meaning, if there is a sign of the invisible, then it is water more than any other single substance that illuminates the way.

This wonder fluid is fit for life on Earth in an absolutely stunning number of ways. It is fit for the formation of proto-planetary discs, for the formation of the planets, for the formation of the oceans, and for their subsequent preservation. Water is uniquely fit for the hydrological cycle, the tectonic cycle, and the temperature regulation of the human body. The properties of water play a critical part in the formation of the great oceanic currents, which circulate crucial nutrients throughout the world ocean. Those currents play a key role in global temperature regulation and moderation and in controlling the CO_2 levels in the atmosphere. Water is superbly and uniquely fit to dissolve the minerals in the rocks, and her great solvation powers are fit for the circulation of nutrients both in the blood stream and in the oceans. Water's expansion on freezing and its other unique thermal properties preserve large bodies of water in the higher latitudes. Water is fit for bioenergetics by providing the proton flows that play such a unique and critical role in the generation of cellular energy. Water's transparency to light is fit for photosynthesis. Water is not only the giver of oxygen, but also uniquely fit for its use in human respiration! Water is fit to allow sunlight to penetrate the atmosphere and light up the savannah, where the San follow the Kudu across the desert. And it is fit to cool the San on the chase.

Water manifests its life-giving magic from the cosmic to the submicroscopic scale. Its stickiness binds together the icy particles of cosmic dust, promoting the formation of planetesimals. Its high surface tension allows a pond skater to walk on water. It also allows water to rise to the

FIGURE 8.1. SEA STORM.

top of trees. This makes possible the manufacture of wood, the making of fire, and the development of metallurgy.

Water operates on time scales of billions of years in preserving the oceans, on the scale of a day in cooling a swimming pool, and in femtoseconds during proton flow. And by providing proton flows, it may be that water was involved not just in the origin of habitable planetary systems, but also in the origin of life itself. Water's fitness is transcendent.

Heaping wonder on wonder, water achieves its universe of purpose with gratuitous panache, manifesting a peerless artistry in innumerable forms—from a snowflake in the Alps to a winter surf crashing on some Hawaiian shore. Water manifests her beauty in an ocean and in a single a drop of rain!

And as we have seen, water's wonder is not just manifest in a vast number of diverse life-giving processes and phenomena, nor in the myriad of beautiful and dramatic forms she adopts. Her wonder is also manifest is the astonishing fact that her particular unique properties are fit for many very different roles.

But even more remarkable are those many instances where a set of very different properties work together to serve very specific vital ends.

Simply put, there is not in all of science a story the equal of the tale of water. The compaction of so many elements of fitness into so tiny a particle of matter—the three-atom molecule which makes up the wonder fluid—transcends any marvel dreamt up in even the most outlandish works of science fiction or in the most unrestrained esoteric visions of any of the seers and mystics of the past.

Perhaps William Blake's vision of a "world in a grain of sand" and "infinity in the palm of your hand" comes close. Or perhaps the Buddhist Sutra that describes the great jewel-net of Indra, a net stretched infinitely in every direction and with every jewel hung on the net reflecting every other jewel, making up an infinite web of interpenetration and connectedness,[3] might capture something of water's wonder, if the jewels in the net are thought of as elements of water's fitness for life, and if we conceive of the entire net compacted into an inconceivably tiny microcosm.

Design?

WHETHER THE remarkable instances in which various properties of water work together to serve a vital end—such as the suite of properties involved in eroding rocks, or the suite of thermal properties involved in temperature regulation—are actually the result of design or not, there is no doubt that they convey a compelling impression of design. Every bit as remarkable, and also highly suggestive of design—perhaps even more so—are those instances where one vital property of water or set of properties is only useful because of another property or set of properties. We have seen many such instances in the previous chapters, and I have referred to them variously as a teleological sequence or teleological hierarchy.

As we saw, water's fitness for the circulatory system is prior to and necessary to exploit water's talents for temperature regulation and heat extraction in complex, warm-blooded organisms such as ourselves. Water's provision of minerals for land-based life, via its suite of talents for eroding the rocks, is of use only because of water's prior and unique ability to exist in three material states in ambient conditions on Earth—an ability that enables the hydrological cycle. Again, the high surface tension and cohesiveness of water involved in drawing water from the roots to the top of trees enables another suite of fitness for photosynthesis in leaves—including water's evaporative cooling of the leaves, which protects them from overheating in the hot sun.

In such teleological sequences, water is both *end* and *means*, exhibiting a design that transcends anything in the realm of the artifact. This is like clothes delivering themselves by their own powers to the shopping mall; like gasoline delivering itself to the filling station. And in those cases where water is involved in regulatory homeostatic loops (the classic case being silicate weathering), water is not just *means* and *end* but is the major means or agent *regulating the end*, like clothes that not only deliver themselves to the mall but also by their own powers adjust their rate of delivery depending on market demand!

In these extraordinary features, water's design for life is transcendent! Nothing in the artificial realm of our own limited designs comes close. Reason recoils at the notion that such designs could be the result of blind, unseeing processes. There is no domain in which astronomer Fred Hoyle's celebrated confession is more appropriate: "A common sense interpretation of the facts suggests… that there are no blind forces worth speaking about in nature."[4]

The design inference cannot be easily avoided by alluding to supposed defects in the fitness of water. A skeptic may claim, for example, that water is not fit for life below 0°C, because when water freezes the formation of ice crystals damages cell structure due to water's expansion upon freezing. Another might point to the fact that there are vast areas of Earth permanently below zero or temporarily below zero in the winter and far from suitable for life. Such facts, it is proposed, demonstrate that water is far from fine-tuned for life on Earth. But even if water possessed a substantially lower freezing point, it is very hard to envisage organisms in the freezer possessing the high metabolic rates that underlie the active lifestyles of organisms such as ourselves. So even if water were a fluid at temperatures lower than 0°C, this would not be relevant for active, warm-blooded organisms like ourselves that maintain body temperatures well above zero.

Moreover, as we have seen, the expansion of water on freezing preserves liquid water in the higher latitudes, allowing aquatic life to thrive through the winter months. Its expansion on freezing in rock crevasses breaks open the rocks, playing a critical role in rock erosion. If the freezing point were significantly lower, no glaciers would grace the great mountain chains, and the erosional benefits of glaciation would be lost.

In fact, life on Earth does and can survive at temperatures well below zero. Polar bears and emperor penguins remain active throughout the Arctic and Antarctic winters. Moreover, many species survive and thrive at temperatures well below zero using cryoprotectants. In some cases they employ supercooling and vitrification to survive being frozen solid, avoiding the destructive effect of ice crystal formation.[5]

Claiming that water is not extremely fit for life because it does not exist as a fluid below zero degrees Celsius is equivalent to claiming that a car is badly designed because it cannot fly or ascend a vertical cliff. Of course the car was not designed for such actions. Carbon-based life cannot exist in an active volcano or in the center of a star or in the depths of interstellar space.

Similarly, the reactivity of water has been claimed as a defect, because it tends to promote the breakdown of organic molecules, an activity that might have hindered the prebiotic synthesis of the basic organic constituents of living systems, and the formation of biopolymers such as proteins and nucleic acids.[6] Philip Ball and chemist Steven Benner make this argument,[7] but there are at least two problems with it.

First, the route to life is not understood. The fact that we cannot as yet envisage how life arose is surely not a defect of water but a failure of human knowledge and imagination. Moreover, at least some stages in the origin of life must have occurred in an aqueous environment; and if some researches are to believed, the provision of proton flows,[8] a process unique to water (discussed briefly in Chapter 7), may have played a critical role.

Second, water's reactivity promotes the erosion of rocks—an activity vital to all terrestrial life. It also promotes the turnover of the cell's constituents, enabling the hydrolysis of damaged and misfolded proteins, an essential process vital to the survival of the cell.[9] This was conceded by the authors of a major study sponsored by a number of leading U.S. scientific institutions. As they comment, "The turnover of proteins is important… in any system living in a dynamic environment. Thus, the hydrolytic instability of proteins in water is key to maintaining life."[10]

Another line of evidence which undermines the criticism that water's reactivity diminishes its fitness for life is the increasing evidence that free radicals, which were for many years seen to be hazardous because they promote increased turnover and destruction of the cell's constituents, are actually beneficial. Rather than being harmful, they actually enhance the immune system's ability to fight bacterial infection by scavenging damaged DNA and other cellular macromolecules.[11]

Most of the supposed "defects" of water can be seen, as Guillermo Gonzalez points out, to be the inevitable result of constrained optimization—a concept borrowed from engineering.[12] If you want a nicely compact notebook computer, you can't give it a sixty-inch screen, as nice as big screens are. If you want to build a truck that can tow a giant boat, you're going to have to sacrifice some fuel efficiency. Engineers are *constrained* by trade-offs. But those realities don't mean that the notebook computer or the powerful truck is poorly designed. If you want to erode rocks, water must be reactive to a degree, even though that reactivity may cause an increased turnover of the cell's constituents. If you want a glacier to grind down rocks, then water needs to freeze, even though the freezing may destroy the delicate fabric of cells exposed to temperatures below zero. The claim that water is not well-tuned for life, because a less reactive water would be better in some respects for the origin of life, loses its force when seen through the lens of constrained optimization reasoning.

Unique Fitness

EVEN IF the design inference is rejected by recourse to supposed defects in the fitness of water, or by appealing to the increasingly popular notion of an infinity of worlds—a notion that goes back to pre-Socratic times but has been reformulated in the modern conception of a multiverse[13]—what is not in doubt is that whatever views we may entertain as to its ultimate causation, water is uniquely fit to a very remarkable degree for life as it exists on Earth.

On this count the evidence is unequivocal. As Henderson noted more than a century ago, nothing can compare with water as the medium of life.[14] On the evidence available, no other fluid known to science could stand in for water. No other fluid has a fraction of the ensemble of fitness for carbon-based life. The ensemble includes fitness for phenomena as diverse as melting the mantle, animating ocean currents, cooling the body, and providing an ideal buffer for maintaining acid-base homeostasis. It's a fitness manifested both on a scale of hundreds of kilometers over millions of years, and on a scale of nanometers over mere microseconds. As is so often true, and nowhere more than in the case of water, proven fact is more incredible than fiction.

And almost certainly there are more elements of fitness yet to be discovered. The trend of scientific discovery bears this out. Since the early nineteenth century, when only the fitness of water's thermal, solvation, and freezing properties had been documented, successive advances have relentlessly revealed additional elements of fitness. There are clearly more to come—probably many more. It could even turn out that what we know presently of water's fitness for life is only a tiny fraction of the complete story.

Of course, because water is a liquid, clearly some of its properties are generic properties of all fluids. In Chapter 6 mention was made of water's incompressibility—essential if a substance is to form the medium of the circulatory system—which as pointed out is a property of all fluids and not a unique property of water. Similarly, in restricted domains many fluids may possess properties similar to those of water. For example, as Ball points out, some other fluids, such as ethane, foramide, and liquid ammonia, are also good solvents.[15]

But even if some liquids possess comparable properties to water in some domains, where water is absolutely peerless is in the sheer number of diverse elements of fitness for life on Earth and in the way ensembles of properties work together to achieve vital ends. Even if another solvent might stand in for water, or even better it in restricted domains and for very specific ends,[16] no known fluid possesses anything remotely comparable with the depth and breadth of water's fitness for life on Earth.

And not only is water's fitness for carbon-based life on Earth peerless. I think we can infer something else, something much more radical—that given the vast inventory of diverse elements of water's fitness for life on Earth, it is practically certain that no other fluid exists—not ethane, foramide, liquid ammonia, or other candidates mentioned by Ball[17]—which might form the medium for some other alien biochemistry that would be remotely as fit for that hypothetical alien biochemistry as water is for Earth's carbon-based life.

Summary

WE HAVE traveled a long way with water from when we stood spellbound before the Bridalveil Fall and wondered at our strange and fateful connection with those falling waters. As we have seen in this book, water grants us life not just by its tireless work in the fall, not just in its fitness to form the matrix of our blood, but in a myriad of additional ways.

The very topology of the Yosemite Valley itself is the result of water's many talents—to move tectonic plates, to form continental crust in the hot, deep forge above subduction zones, to shave the sheer walls of the valley by glacial bulldozing, and so on. Further, both the existence of the valley and our ability to gaze upon its beauty depend on a vital chain of fitness and coincidences in the properties of water, a chain that begins by making stardust and extends to the folding of a protein. In this ensemble of fitness for life, an ensemble touching nearly every aspect of the natural order, our own being and becoming is linked to every aspect of the fabric of the world. In the properties of water the cosmos is revealed to be a transcendent unity, with life on Earth and beings of our biological design as its central aim and focus.

The unique fitness of nature for life on Earth and for beings of our biology, manifested so spectacularly in the properties of water, is a scientific discovery, whatever the ultimate cause of that fitness may be, whether by design or not. The discovery is an ontological revelation about the essential nature of the universe and the place of life and man within the ultimate fabric of being. The revelation that the laws of nature—as manifested in the fitness of water for life on Earth and for our biology—are uniquely fine-tuned for our existence is true regardless of whether there is life on other planets or only on Earth. It is true even if the fitness is deemed to be imperfect. It is true even if some other fluids possess some properties similar to those of water. It is true even if there exist other primitive life forms based on exotic alien chemistries thriving in, say, hydrocarbon lakes. It is true even if an immensely fortuitous but blind concourse of atoms played a role in the emergence of life on Earth.

Thomas Huxley famously wrote, "The question of questions for mankind—the problem which underlies all others, and is more deeply interesting than any other   is the ascertainment of the place which Man occupies in nature and of his relations to the universe of things."[18]

The focus throughout this book has been to provide an answer to Huxley's grand "question of questions." And it is water's special fitness for life on Earth and for beings of our biological design that provides a definitive answer. Water has testified, and its testimony is unequivocal. Life and humankind do occupy, after all, a unique place in the natural order. Water, the peerless matrix, sings a song of life on Earth and of humankind, its properties fine-tuned for our type of life from the moment of creation, its wondrous fitness for our being long ago inscribed into the cosmic order. In water's magic, the Copernican principle is well and truly overturned.

Endnotes

1. The Water Wheel

1. Richard Bentley, *The Folly and Unreasonableness of Atheism* (printed version of eight sermons), (London: Printed by J. H. for H. Mortlock, 1699), 265. Available at https://archive.org/stream/follyandunreaso00bentgoog#page/n271/mode/2up/search/circulation+

2. The introductory paragraphs are from Michael J. Denton, *Nature's Destiny* (New York: Simon and Schuster, 1998), 22.

3. Philip Ball, *H_2O: A Biography of Water* (London: Weidenfeld and Nicolson, 1999), 26. [Note: In this quoted passage, as in most quoted passages throughout this book, internal references have been removed.]

4. Andrew P. Jephcoat, "Rare gas solids in the Earth's deep interior," *Nature* 393, no. 355–358 (May 28, 1998). doi:10.1038/30712.

5. Even CO_2, which freezes at –78°C, exists on Earth only as a gas, as the partial pressure of CO_2 is so low that the rate of sublimation greatly exceeds the rate of condensation. See Anthony Watts, "Results: Lab experiment regarding CO_2 'snow' in Antarctica at –113°F (-80°C) —not possible," *Watts Up With That?*, June 13, 2009 (accessed March 29, 2017), https://wattsupwiththat.com/2009/06/13/results-lab-experiment-regarding-co2-snow-in-antarctica-at-113%C2%B0f-80-5%C2%B0c-not-possible/.

6. Albert Szent-Györgyi, *The Living State: With Observations on Cancer* (New York; London: Academic Press,1972), 9.

7. Ball, *H_2O*, 26.

8. Ibid., 23–25.

9. Ibid., 26.

10. Marcia Bjornerud, *Reading the Rocks: The Autobiography of Earth* (New York: Basic Books, 2005), 73.

11. Lawrence Henderson, *The Fitness of the Environment: An Inquiry into the Biological Significance of the Properties of Matter* (New York: The Macmillan Company, 1913), 114.

12. Ibid., 113.

13. Felix Franks, "Water the Unique Chemical," in *Water a Comprehensive Treatise*, ed. Felix Franks, vol. 1 (New York: Plenum Press, 1972), 20.

14. For more information, see, "Gallium," *Wikipedia: The Free Encyclopedia*, The Wikimedia Foundation, June 19, 2017, accessed June 22, 2017, https://en.wikipedia.org/wiki/Gallium.

15. Glenn Elert, "Viscosity," *The Physics Hypertextbook*, 2017, accessed June 22, 2017, http://physics.info/viscosity/.

16. Yaolin Shi and Jianling Cao, "Lithosphere Effective Viscosity of Continental China," *Earth Science Frontiers* 15, no. 3 (May 2008): 82–95. doi:10.1016/S1872-5791(08)60064-0.

17. "Niagara Falls," *Geology*, New York State Museum, 2017, accessed June 22, 2017, http://www.nysm.nysed.gov/research-collections/geology/resources/niagara-falls.

18. Gerard V. Middleton and Peter R. Wilcock, *Mechanics in the Earth and Environmental Sciences* (Cambridge; New York: Cambridge University Press, 1994), 84.

19. Michael Pidwirny provides a helpful introduction. He writes, "The movement of ice over the ground in most temperate glaciers is enhanced by a process known as basal sliding. The immense pressure caused by the weight of the overlying glacial mass causes the ice making contact with the ground to melt because of pressure, despite subzero temperatures (pressure melting). The melting ice then forms a layer of water that reduces the friction between the glacial ice and the ground surface. This water then facilitates the movement of the ice over the ground surface by producing a layer with very little friction. Because of basal sliding, some glaciers can move up to 50 meters in one day. However, average rates of movement are usually less than 1 meter per day." Michael Pidwirny, "Glacial Processes," *Fundamentals of Physical Geography* (2nd edition, 2006), accessed March 29, 2017, available at http://www.physicalgeography.net/fundamentals/10ae.html.

20. Ibid.

21. Nyle C. Brady and Raymond Weil, *Elements of the Nature and Properties of Soils*, 15th edition (Harlow, Essex: Pearson Education Limited, 2016), 22.

22. Ibid., 22.

23. Ibid., 25.

24. Nyle C. Brady and Raymond R. Weil, *The Nature and Properties of Soils* (New Jersey: Prentice Hall, 1996), 242.

25. Ibid., 241.

26. Ibid., 270.

27. Ball, H_2O, 27.

28. J. C. I. Dooge, "Concepts of the hydrological cycle. Ancient and Modern," *International Symposium on OH_2 'Origins and History of Hydrology'*, Dijon, May 9–11, 2001, available online here http://hydrologie.org/ACT/OH2/actes/03_dooge.pdf. Authors in China also grasped the essential elements of the cycle, as Dooge points out [page 3]: "Lu Shih Ch'un Ch'iu (239 B.C.) wrote: 'The clouds go westward and never come to an end, no matter whether it's a summer or a winter. The rivers flow eastwards and never cease to flow regardless of it being night or day,' and later writes: 'The small streams become large and the heavy waters in the seas become light and mount to the clouds. This is part of the Rotation of the Tao (Cycle).'"

29. Leonardo da Vinci, quoted in Dooge, op. cit., 5.

30. Ibid., 7. As Dooge points out (page 8), by carefully calculating the amount of rainfall from several gauges in England and Wales and estimating the total run off over the same areas, Dalton was able to show that rainfall was sufficient to supply rivers and streams with water. Dalton concluded: "Upon the whole then I think that we can finally conclude that the rain and dew of this country are equivalent to the quantity

of water carried off by evaporation and by the rivers. And as nature acts upon general laws, we ought to infer, that it must be the case in every other country till the contrary is proved."

31. Yi-Fu Tuan, *The Hydrologic Cycle and the Wisdom of God* (Toronto: University of Toronto Press, 1968).

32. Ibid., 130.

33. John Ray, *The Wisdom of God Manifested in the Works of Creation* (London: W&J Innys, 1743), 89. Available at https://archive.org/details/wisdomofgodmanif00ray.

34. Ibid., 90.

35. Ibid.

36. Tuan, 4.

37. Ibid, 4–6.

38. P. C. W. Davies, *The Cosmic Blueprint: New Discoveries in Nature's Creative Ability to Order the Universe* (New York: Simon and Schuster, 1988), 201.

2. TECTONIC RECYCLING

1. Roberto F. Weinberg and Pavlína Hasalová, "Water-Fluxed Melting of the Continental Crust: A Review," *Lithos* 212–215 (January 2015): 158–88. doi:10.1016/j.lithos.2014.08.021.

2. Nick W. Rogers, ed., *An Introduction to Our Dynamic Planet* (New York: The Open University / Cambridge: Cambridge University Press, 2008), 310.

3. Douglas W. Burbank, John Leland, Eric Fielding, Robert S. Anderson, Nicholas Brozovic, Mary R. Reid, and Christopher Duncan, "Bedrock Incision, Rock Uplift and Threshold Hillslopes in the Northwestern Himalayas," *Nature* 379, no. 6565 (February 8, 1996): 505–10. doi:10.1038/379505a0.

4. D.-G. Shu, S. Conway Morris, J. Han, Z.-F. Zhang, K. Yasui, P. Janvier, L. Chen, et al., "Head and Backbone of the Early Cambrian Vertebrate Haikouichthys," *Nature* 421, no. 6922 (January 30, 2003): 526–29. doi:10.1038/nature01264.

5. H. Holland, *The Chemical Evolution of the Atmosphere and Oceans* (Princeton: Princeton University Press, 1984), xi; James Lovelock, *Gaia: A New Look at Life on Earth* (New York: Oxford University Press, 2000). See Chapter 6 for discussion of the constant salinity of the sea through geological time.

6. For more information, see: Ward E. Sanford, Michael W. Doughten, Tyler B. Coplen, Andrew G. Hunt, and Thomas D. Bullen, "Evidence for High Salinity of Early Cretaceous Sea Water from the Chesapeake Bay Crater," *Nature* 503, no. 7475 (November 13, 2013): 252–56, doi:10.1038/nature12714; R. A. Berner, "The Rise of Plants and Their Effect on Weathering and Atmosphere," *Science* 276 (1997): 544–46; Elisabetta Erba, Cinzia Bottini, Helmut J. Weissert, and Christina E. Keller, "Calcareous Nannoplankton Response to Surface-Water Acidification around Oceanic Anoxic Event 1a," *Science* (New York, N.Y.) 329, no. 5990 (July 23, 2010): 428–32, doi:10.1126/science.1188886. For a more popular version of this work, see David Biello, "Ancient Ocean Acidification Intimates Long Recovery from Climate Change," *Scientific American*, July 22, 2010, https://www.scientificamerican.

com/article/ancient-ocean-acidification-intimates-long-recovery-from-climate-change/.

7. Michael E. Q. Pilson, *An Introduction to the Chemistry of the Sea*, second ed. (Cambridge: Cambridge University Press, 2013), 396 and ch. 15. See also Lovelock, *Gaia*.

8. Rachel Carson, *The Sea Around Us* (New York: Oxford University Press, 2003), 97.

9. Steve A. Thorpe, ed. *Elements of Physical Oceanography: A Derivative of Encyclopedia of Ocean Sciences*, 2nd ed. (Boston: Elsevier, 2009), 524.

10. Rogers et al., *An Introduction to Our Dynamic Planet*, chapter 3; Tom Garrison, *Oceanography: An Invitation to Marine Science with Additional Readings*, 7th ed. (Belmont, CA: Brooks/Cole, Cengage Learning, 2010), chapter 3.

11. Hazel Rymer, "Global Outlooks," *Nature* 383, no. 6602 (October 1996): 684.

12. Marcia Bjornerud, *Reading the Rocks: The Autobiography of Earth* (New York: Basic Books, 2005), 20.

13. Ibid., 19–20.

14. D. Craw, P. O. Koons, D. Winslow, C. P. Chamberlain, and P. Zeitler, "Boiling Fluids in a Region of Rapid Uplift, Nanga Parbat Massif, Pakistan," *Earth and Planetary Science Letters* 128, nos. 3–4 (December 1994): 169–82, doi:10.1016/0012-821X(94)90143; "The Himalayas: Two Continents Collide," *USGS*, United States Geological Survey, September 3, 2015, accessed June 22, 2017, https://pubs.usgs.gov/gip/dynamic/himalaya.html. The New Zealand Alps are also rising at ten mm p.a.; see "Tectonic Uplift," *GNS Science*, accessed June 22, 2017, https://www.gns.cri.nz/Home/Learning/Science-Topics/Landforms/Mountains-and-Uplift/Tectonic-uplift.

15. Bjornerud, 114.

16. For a lucid description of plate tectonics see: Tom Garrison, *Oceanography: An Invitation to Marine Science with Additional Readings*, chapter 3; Rogers, ed., *An Introduction to Our Dynamic Planet*, chapters 3 and 4; Jonathan Irving Lunine, *Earth: Evolution of a Habitable World*, 2nd ed. (Cambridge: Cambridge University Press, 2013), chapters 9 and 16; and Wolfgang Frisch, Martin Meschede, and Ronald C. Blakey, *Plate Tectonics, Continental Drift and Mountain Building* (Berlin; Heidelberg: Springer-Verlag, 2011), 70, http://site.ebrary.com/id/10427938. Another brief but succinct description of plate tectonics is given in Frank Press and Raymond Siever, *Earth*, 4th ed. (New York: W. H. Freeman, 1986), prologue and pages 17–20.

17. From Rogers et al., *An Introduction to Our Dynamic Planet*, 42. The authors comment: "The Earth is composed of solid rocks that behave in a rigid way, and that is certainly correct on length scales of metres and kilometres, but that style of behavior breaks down over longer length scales and in the mantle where temperatures are much higher. At depth, rocks begin to behave more as fluids than as rigid solids, and when loaded with ice sheets, volcanoes or mountains they begin to flow. This leads to a new mechanical, as opposed to compositional, division of the outer layers of the Earth… The rigid cold surface layer [made up of the tectonic plates] is known as the lithosphere… Below this is the more mobile… asthenosphere [upper mantle]… which can deform like a viscous fluid when under stress."

18. See "The Crust and Lithosphere," *The Geological Society*, 2012 (accessed March 29, 2017), http://www.geolsoc.org.uk/Education-and-Careers/Resources/Papers-

and-Reports/Flood-basalts-mantle-plumes-and-mass-extinctions/The-Crust-and-Lithosphere.

19. Press and Siever, 19.

20. H. Frankel, "The Continental Drift Debate," in *Scientific Controversies: Case Solutions in the Resolution and Closure of Disputes in Science and Technology*, ed. H. T. Engelhardt Jr. and A. L. Caplan (Cambridge; New York; Port Chester; Melbourne; Sydney: Cambridge University Press, 1987), 203–248.

21. Ibid.

22. Bjornerud, 119.

23. Rogers et al., *An Introduction to Our Dynamic Planet*, 310–312.

24. Ibid., 310: "Incorporation of H_2O in silicate lattices is accomplished through two substitution mechanisms involving hydrogen ions (H +). The first of these involves the direct replacement of Mg2+ with 2H+. This is the most common substitution, because ALL mantle silicates contain Mg. The second mechanism involves the coupled substitution H+ and Al3+ replacing Si4+ in aluminium-bearing minerals, such as pyroxenes, particularly garnet. The introduction of water into the crystal structure of olivine may also replace oxygen atoms with OH-."

25. Ibid., 311.

26. Ibid. 311–312.

27. P. D. Asimow and C. H. Langmuir, "The Importance of Water to Oceanic Mantle Melting Regimes," *Nature* 421, no. 6925 (February 20, 2003): 815–20, doi:10.1038/nature01429; Rogers et al., see section 5.4.

28. Rogers et al., *An Introduction to Our Dynamic Planet*, 208.

29. Erik Kemetti, "Why Do Rocks Melt on Earth Anyway?" *Wired*, December 19, 2012 (accessed March 29, 2017), https://www.wired.com/2012/12/why-do-rocks-melt-volcano/.

30. Lunine, 193.

31. Timothy H. Dixon, and J. Casey Moore, eds., *The Seismogenic Zone of Subduction Thrust Faults*, MARGINS Theoretical and Experimental Earth Science Series (New York: Columbia University Press, 2007), 592; Rogers et al., *An Introduction to Our Dynamic Planet*, 304.

32. Wolfgang Frisch, Martin Meschede, and Ronald Blakey, *Plate Tectonics: Continental Drift and Mountain Building* (Berlin: Springer-Verlag, 2011), 70.

33. Jacqueline Eaby Dixon, Loretta Leist, Charles Langmuir, and Jean-Guy Schilling, "Recycled Dehydrated Lithosphere Observed in Plume-Influenced Mid-Ocean-Ridge Basalt," *Nature* 420, no. 6914 (November 28, 2002): 385–89. doi:10.1038/nature01215.

34. "In a million years each kilometre along the length of this subduction zone would therefore transfer between 170 to 318 billion tonnes of water into the mantle; an estimate more than ten times previous estimates. The authors observe that at such a rate a subduction zone equivalent to the existing, 3400 km long Kuril and Izu-Bonin arcs that affect Japan would have transferred sufficient water to fill the present world oceans 3.5 times over the history of the Earth. Had the entire rate of modern subduction along a length of 55 thousand kilometres been maintained over 4.5 billion years, the world's oceans would have been recycled through the mantle

once every 80 million years. To put that in perspective, since the Cretaceous Chalk of southern England began to be deposited, the entire mass of ocean water has been renewed. Moreover, subduction has probably slowed considerably through time, so the transfer of water would have been at a greater pace in the more distant past." Steve Drury, "Subduction and the Water Cycle," *earth-pages*, February 11, 2014 (accessed March 29, 2017), https://earth-pages.co.uk/2014/02/11/subduction-and-the-water-cycle/.

35. Rogers et al, 310.

36. Martha R. Scott, "Ocean Chemical Processes," *Water Encyclopedia*, 2017 (accessed March 29, 2017), http://www.waterencyclopedia.com/Mi-Oc/Ocean-Chemical-Processes.html.

37. Tom Garrison, personal communication.

38. Rogers et al., 193–194.

39. Tom Garrison, personal communication, March 3, 2012.

40. L. Paul Knauth, "Temperature and salinity history of the Precambrian ocean: Implications for the course of microbial evolution," *Palaeogeography, Palaeoclimatology, Palaeoecology* 219 (2005): 53–69. Available at http://ahealedplanet.net/Knauth.pdf.

41. Rogers et al., 319.

42. Lunine, see section 16.4.3.

43. Bjornerud, 115.

44. Lunine, 194.

45. Ibid; See also James A. Whitney, "The Origin of Granite: The Role and Source of Water in the Evolution of Granitic Magmas," *Geological Society of America Bulletin* 100, no. 12 (December 1988): 1886–97, doi:10.1130/0016-7606(1988)100<1886:TOOGTR>2.3.CO;2; I. H. Campbell and S. R. Taylor, "No water, no granites—No oceans, no continents," *Geophysical Research Letters* 10 (1983): 1061–1064; M. Stein and Z. Ben-Avraham, "Mechanisms of Continental Crust Growth," in *Treatise on Geophysics*, ed. Gerald Schubert (Amsterdam: Elsevier, 2007), 171–95, doi:10.1016/B978-044452748-6.00144-9.

Jonathan Lunine comments (op. cit., 193): "What is required to make more felsic rocks [granitic continental crust] is the addition of a material that will alter the melting relationship of the basalt, and water is an excellent candidate… in the presence of sufficient amounts of water the melting point of the basalt drops dramatically. Further the melting is partial, with larger ions again partitioning preferably into the melt."

46. Campbell and Taylor.

47. Stein and Avraham, 177.

48. Bjornerud, 126.

49. Ibid., 127.

50. Ibid.

51. Ibid.

52. Personal communication with Tom Garrison (13/3/2012).

53. Philip Ball, H_2O: *A Biography of Water* (London: Weidenfeld and Nicolson, 1999), 23.

54. Bjornerud, 115.

55. Ibid. 130–131.

56. "If God did not exist, it would be necessary to invent him." Voltaire, in "Épître à l'Auteur du Livre des Trois Imposteurs," *OEuvres complètes de Voltaire*, ed. Louis Moland (Paris: Garnier, 1877–1885), tome 10, pp. 402–405.

57. Immanuel Kant, *Critique of Judgement*, trans. J. H. Bernard (London: Macmillan and Co., 1914). Available at: https://archive.org/stream/cu31924028104085#page/n5/mode/2up/search/unity.

58. Ibid., 278.

59. Ibid.

60. Ibid., 279.

61. Ibid., 280.

62. Bjornerud, 131.

3. Preserving the Ocean

1. "The Solar System and Beyond is Awash in Water," *NASA*, November 21, 2016 (accessed March 30, 2017), http://www.nasa.gov/jpl/the-solar-system-and-beyond-is-awash-in-water.

2. James Lovelock, *Gaia: A New Look at Life on Earth* (Oxford; New York: Oxford University Press, 2000), Preface, vii.

3. Kevin Lepot, Karim Benzerara, Gordon E. Brown, and Pascal Philippot, "Microbially Influenced Formation of 2,724-Million-Year-Old Stromatolites," *Nature Geoscience* 1, no. 2 (February 2008): 118–21. doi:10.1038/ngeo107.

4. Donald R. Lowe, "Stromatolites 3,400-Myr Old from the Archean of Western Australia," *Nature* 284, no. 5755 (April 3, 1980): 441–43. doi:10.1038/284441a0.

5. Carolyn Gramling, "Hints of Oldest Fossil Life Found in Greenland Rocks," *Science*, AAAS, August 31, 2016 (accessed March 30, 2017). doi:10.1126/science.aah7251.

6. Lovelock, Chapter 2, 18, 25.

7. Donald U. Wise, "Freeboard of Continents Through Time," *Geological Society of America Memoirs* 132 (1972): 87–100, available at http://memoirs.gsapubs.org/lookup/doi/10.1130/MEM132-p87; James F. Kasting and Nils G. Holm, "What Determines the Volume of the Oceans?" *Earth and Planetary Science Letters* 109, no. 3–4 (April 1992): 507–15, doi:10.1016/0012-821X(92)90110-H; Michael E. Q. Pilson, *An Introduction to the Chemistry of the Sea*, second ed. (Cambridge: Cambridge University Press, 2013), 385–386.

8. Marcia Bjornerud, *Reading the Rocks: The Autobiography of the Earth* (Cambridge, MA: Westview Press, a member of the Perseus Books Group, 2005), 8.

9. James Lovelock, *Gaia: A New Look at Life on Earth* (Oxford; New York: Oxford University Press, 2000), Chapter 1.

10. Ewine F. van Dishoeck, "Water in Space," *Europhysics News* 42, no. 1 (January 2011): 26–31. doi:10.1051/epn/2011105.IV.

11. Ewine F. van Dishoek, Edwin Bergin, Dariusz C. Lis, and Jonathan I. Lunine, "Water from Clouds to Planets," in *Protostars and Planets VI*, eds. Henrik Beuther, Ralf S. Klessen, Cornelis P. Dullemond, and Thomas Henning (Tucson: The University of Arizona Press; Lunar and Planetary Institute, 2014), 835–858. The paper describes the path that water takes from contracting interstellar clouds to the surfaces of planets. This doesn't mean that water is essential in the formation of planets; there are other coolants in interstellar clouds besides water. However, it is safe to say that water plays a role, even if we can't say at this time that it is essential.

12. B. Gundlach and J. Blum, "The Stickiness of Micrometer-Sized Water-Ice Particles," *The Astrophysical Journal* 798, no. 1 (December 18, 2014): 34. doi:10.1088/0004-637X/798/1/34. The authors comment:

    "[E]xperiments investigating the stickiness of water ice have been scarce, particularly in the astrophysically relevant micrometer-sized region and at low temperatures. In this work, we present an experimental setup to grow aggregates composed of μm-sized water-ice particles, which we used to measure the sticking and erosion thresholds of the ice particles at different temperatures between 114 K and 260 K. We show with our experiments that for low temperatures (below 210 K), μm-sized water-ice particles stick below a threshold velocity of 9.6ms^{-1}, which is approximately 10 times higher than the sticking threshold of μm-sized silica particles. Furthermore, erosion of the grown ice aggregates is observed for velocities above 15.3ms^{-1}".

13. Philip Ball, *H$_2$O: A Biography of Water* (London: Weidenfeld and Nicolson, 1999), 16.

14. For more on water and other coolants involved in star formation, see "Star Formation and the Cooling of Molecular Clouds," The Submillimeter Wave Astronomy Satellite (SWAS), https://www.cfa.harvard.edu/swas/science1.html (last accessed June 23, 2017).

15. Guillermo Gonzalez, "Setting the Stage for Habitable Planets," *Life* (Basel) 4, no. 1 (March 2014): 35–65. Available online at https://www.ncbi.nlm.nih.gov/pmc/articles/PMC4187148/. Gonzalez notes that the presence of giant planets is observed to correlate strongly with metallicity (and here metals are defined as everything beyond hydrogen and helium), and he argues that a good case can be made that giant planets are required for a planetary system to be as habitable as our Solar System. Thus, while terrestrial planets probably can form around a star from metal-poor interstellar clouds, those terrestrial planets are unlikely to be habitable due to the planetary system's lack of giant planets.

16 Bjornerud, 114.

17. Ibid.

18. Brandon Schmandt, Steven D. Jacobsen, Thorsten W. Becker, Zhenxian Liu, and Kenneth G. Dueker, "Dehydration melting at the top of the lower mantle," *Science* 344, no. 6189 (June 13, 2014): 1265–1268, doi:10.1126/science.1253358; "Rare Diamond confirms that Earth's mantle holds an ocean's worth of water," *Scientific American*, March 12, 2014.

19. Perry Samson, "Evolution of the Atmosphere: Composition, Structure and Energy," *Global Change: The Science of Sustainability*, University of Michigan (accessed March 30, 2017), http://www.globalchange.umich.edu/globalchange1/current/lectures/Perry_Samson_lectures/evolution_atm/.

20. Bjornerud, 115.

21. Ibid.

22. H. Rickman et al., "Cometary Impact Rates on the Moon and Planets During the Late Heavy Bombardment," *Astronomy & Astrophysics*, Vol. 598; Marty Bernard et al., "Origins of volatile elements (H, C, N, Noble Gases) on Earth and Mars in Light of Recent Results from the ROSETTA Cometary Mission," *Earth and Planetary Science Letters*, Vol. 441, 91–102; Charles Q. Choi, "Most of Earth's Water Came from Asteroids, Not Comets," Dec. 10, 2014, *Space.com*, available at http://www.space.com/27969-earth-water-from-asteroids-not-comets.html (Last accessed June 5, 2017).

23. Tim Lenton, and A. J. Watson, *Revolutions That Made the Earth* (Oxford; New York: Oxford University Press, 2011), 107. For discussion of faint young sun paradox, see Sanjoy M. Som, David C. Catling, Jelte P. Harnmeijer, Peter M. Polivka, and Roger Buick, "Air Density 2.7 Billion Years Ago Limited to Less than Twice Modern Levels by Fossil Raindrop Imprints," *Nature* 484, no. 7394 (March 28, 2012): 359–62. doi:10.1038/nature10890. Abstract available at http://www.nature.com/nature/journal/v484/n7394/abs/nature10890.html.

24. S. Elser, B. Moore, J. Stadel, and R. Morishima, "How Common Are Earth–Moon Planetary Systems?" *Icarus* 214, no. 2 (August 2011): 357–65. doi:10.1016/j.icarus.2011.05.025. From the abstract of their paper: "The Earth's comparatively massive moon, formed via a giant impact on the proto-Earth, has played an important role in the development of life on our planet, both in the history and strength of the ocean tides and in stabilizing the chaotic spin of our planet."

25. R. Brasser et al., "A Dynamical Study on the Habitability of Terrestrial Exoplanets—I. Tidally Evolved Planet-Satellite Pairs," *Monthly Notices of the Royal Astronomical Society*, 2013, 428:1673–1685. doi: 10.1093/mnras/sts151.

26. Guillermo Gonzalez, "Setting the Stage"; Oleg G. Sorokhtin, George V. Chilingarian, and Nikolaĭ Olegovich Sorokhtin, *Evolution of Earth and Its Climate: Birth, Life and Death of Earth, Developments in Earth and Environmental Sciences* 10 (Amsterdam: Elsevier, 2011), 525–526.

27. P. F. Hoffman, A. J. Kaufman, G. P. Halverson, and D. P. Schrag, "A Neoproterozoic snowball Earth," *Science* 281 (1998): 1342–46; P. F. Hoffman and D. P. Schrag, "Snowball Earth," *Scientific American* 282 (2000): 68–75.

28. P. C. Lippert, "Big Discovery for Biogenic Magnetite," *Proceedings of the National Academy of Sciences* 105, no. 46 (November 18, 2008): 17595–96. doi:10.1073/pnas.0809839105.

29. P. Schulte, L. Alegret, I. Arenillas, J. A. Arz, P. J. Barton, P. R. Bown, T. J. Bralower, et al., "The Chicxulub Asteroid Impact and Mass Extinction at the Cretaceous-Paleogene Boundary," *Science* 327, no. 5970 (March 5, 2010): 1214–18. doi:10.1126/science.1177265.

30. Bjornerud, 6.

31. Described in Jonathan Irving Lunine, *Earth: Evolution of a Habitable World*, 2nd ed. (Cambridge: Cambridge Univ. Press, 2013), section 14.7; this was one of the first papers to consider silicate weathering as a means of temperature/CO_2 regulation. See also James C. G. Walker, P. B. Hays, and J. F. Kasting, "A Negative Feedback Mechanism for the Long-Term Stabilization of Earth's Surface

Temperature," *Journal of Geophysical Research* 86, no. C10 (1981): 9776. doi:10.1029/JC086iC10p09776. For a recent review see Lee R. Kump, Susan L. Brantley, and Michael A. Arthur, "Chemical Weathering, Atmospheric CO_2, and Climate," *Annual Review of Earth and Planetary Sciences* 28, no. 1 (May 2000): 611–67. doi:10.1146/annurev.earth.28.1.611.

32. Stephen Harding and L. Margulis, "Water Gaia: A 3.5 Thousand Million Years of Wetness on Planet Earth," in *Gaia in Turmoil: Climate Change, Biodepletion, and Earth Ethics in an Age of Crisis*, Eileen Crist and H. Bruce Rinker, eds. (Cambridge, Mass: MIT Press, 2010), 41–59. The authors defend a 'Gaian view' of water's retention on earth. They entitle their thesis: 'Life Retained Planetary Water.'

33. Hoffman et al. (1998).

34. Lippert (2008).

35. Bjornerud, 13.

36. Bjornerud, 13.

37. Lunine (2013), section 15.2.1, page 179; Lenton and Watson, 68.

38. Harding and Margulis, "Water Gaia: A 3.5 Thousand Million Years of Wetness on Planet Earth."

39. Although not a property of water, it is worth pointing out in passing that it is fortunate indeed that silicon and oxygen are among the commonest elements in the universe and in the earth's crust, since without an endless supply of silicates the mechanism would grind to a halt.

40. N. N. Greenwood, and A. Earnshaw, *Chemistry of the Elements*, 2nd ed. (Oxford; Boston: Butterworth-Heinemann, 1997), 223–224. See also physical properties of gallium, bismuth and silicon listed: "Gallium," *Wikipedia: The Free Encyclopedia*, The Wikimedia Foundation, June 19, 2017, accessed June 22, 2017, https://en.wikipedia.org/wiki/Gallium; "Bismuth," *Wikipedia: The Free Encyclopedia*, June 18, 2017, accessed June 22, 2017, https://en.wikipedia.org/wiki/Bismuth; "Silicon," *Wikipedia: The Free Encyclopedia*, The Wikimedia Foundation, June 13, 2017, accessed June 22, 2017, https://en.wikipedia.org/wiki/Silicon.

41. Lawrence Henderson, *The Fitness of the Environment: An Inquiry into the Biological Significance of the Properties of Matter* (New York: The Macmillan Company, 1913), 80–91; A. E. Needham, *The Uniqueness of Biological Materials* (Oxford: Pergamon Press, 1965), 15.

42. H. S. Jeon, "Anomalous and Unique Properties of Water," *Hemato Institute*, October 12, 2011 (accessed March 30, 2017), http://hematoinstitute.com/articles.php; Martin Chaplin, "Anomalous Properties of Water," *Water Structure and Science*, March 28, 2017 (accessed March 30, 2017), http://www1.lsbu.ac.uk/water/anmlies.html.

43. Henderson, 95–96; Needham, 15.

44. See "Ice – Thermal Properties," *The Engineering ToolBox* (accessed March 30, 2017), http://www.engineeringtoolbox.com/ice-thermal-properties-d_576.html. The thermal conductivity of ice is very low compared to many other solids—two hundred times less than silver and only about three times that of water, a fluid with a higher conductivity than most fluids.

45. Gerard V. Middleton and Peter R. Wilcock, *Mechanics in the Earth and Environmental Sciences*, (Cambridge; New York: Cambridge University Press, 1994), 84.

46. Tom Garrison, *Oceanography: An Invitation to Marine Science with Additional Readings*, 7th ed. (Belmont, CA: Brooks/Cole, Cengage Learning, 2009), 254.

47. Garrison, 254.

48. Ibid.

49. See Garrison, chapter 9, for a description of the deep ocean currents. See page 248 for comments on the Humboldt current.

50. See Peter Wadhams, "How Does Arctic Sea Ice Form and Decay?" *PMEL Arctic Zone*, National Oceanic and Atmospheric Administration, United States Department of Commerce, January 1, 2003 (accessed March 30, 2017), http://www.pmel.noaa.gov/arctic-zone/essay_wadhams.html.

51. Garrison, chapter 9; Wadhams, "How Does Arctic Sea Ice Form and Decay?"

52. Needham, 13 and 15.

53. John M. Wallace and Peter Victor Hobbs, *Atmospheric Science: An Introductory Survey*, 2nd ed. International Geophysics Series 92 (Amsterdam; Boston: Elsevier Academic Press, 2006), section 1.3.4, fig 1.9; Lunine, section 15.2.1.

54. Lenton and Watson, 68.

55. Wallace and Hobbs, section 1.3.4.; Lunine, section 15.2.1, 179.

56. Lenton and Watson, 67–68.

57. Geoffrey K. Vallis, *Climate and Oceans* (Princeton, New Jersey: Princeton UP, 2012). See page 218 in the glossary, where he notes, "Without this effect [the greenhouse], Earth's surface would have a temperature of about 255 K (-1°8C), about 33 degrees lower than it actually is."

58. "Greenhouse gas," *Wikipedia: The Free Encyclopedia*, The Wikipedia Foundation, March 25, 2017 (accessed March 30, 2017), https://en.wikipedia.org/wiki/Greenhouse_gas.

59. Ibid.

60. Donald U. Wise, "Freeboard of Continents Through Time," in *Geological Society of America Memoirs*, vol. 132 (Geological Society of America, 1972), 87–100, see http://memoirs.gsapubs.org/lookup/doi/10.1130/MEM132-p87; Pilson, 396: "The usual assumption is that the total mass of water on the surface of the earth has not changed much since early evidence of water at about 4000 million years ago."

61. Wise, "Freeboard of Continents."

62. James F. Kasting and Nils G. Holm, "What Determines the Volume of the Oceans?" *Earth and Planetary Science Letters* 109, no. 3–4 (April 1992): 507–15, doi:10.1016/0012-821X(92)90110-H; Igor Pioro and Sarah Mokry, "Thermophysical Properties at Critical and Supercritical Pressures," In *Heat Transfer—Theoretical Analysis, Experimental Investigations and Industrial Systems*, ed. Aziz Belmiloudi (Rijika, Croatia and Shanghai, China: InTech, 2011), 573–592, available at http://www.intechopen.com/books/heat-transfer-theoretical-analysis-experimental-investigations-and-industrial-systems/thermophysical-properties-at-critical-and-supercritical-pressures.

63. Pioro and Mokry, "Thermophysical Properties at Critical and Supercritical Pressures."

64. X. Cheng and T. Schulenberg, "Heat Transfer at Supercritical Pressures—A literature review and application to an HPLVWR," *Forschungszentrum Karlsruhe: Wissenschaftliche Berichte*, Institute für Kern- und Energietechnik, Programm nukleare Sicherheitsforschung, 2001 (accessed March 30, 2017), http://digbib. ubka.uni-karlsruhe.de/volltexte/fzk/6609/6609.pdf. At a pressure of 25 MPa the pseudo-critical temperature is 384°C. The specific heat at the critical point is as high as 5600 kJ/kg K (see figure 2.3) which is more than 1000 times higher than that at room temperature. Figures 2.4 to 2.7 show some thermal physical properties versus temperature at different pressures.

65. Pioro and Motry.

66. James F. Kasting and Nils G. Holm, "What Determines the Volume of the Oceans?" *Earth and Planetary Science Letters* 109, no. 3–4 (April 1992): 507–15. doi:10.1016/0012-821X(92)90110-H.

67. Ibid.

68. David C. Catling, Christopher R. Glein, Kevin J. Zahnle, and Christopher P. McKay, "Why O2 Is Required by Complex Life on Habitable Planets and the Concept of Planetary 'Oxygenation Time,'" *Astrobiology* 5, no. 3 (June 2005): 415–38. doi:10.1089/ast.2005.5.415.

69. Ball, "Will ET Drink Water?" *Nautilus, Cosmos*, November 2016, accessed June 22, 2017, http://cosmos.nautil.us/feature/21/will-et-.

4. The Climate Machine

1. Marcia Bjornerud, *Reading the Rocks: The Autobiography of the Earth* (Cambridge, MA: Westview Press, a member of the Perseus Books Group, 2005), 7–8.

2. "What affects global climate?" *Met Office*, Met Office UK, 2017 (accessed March 30, 2017), http://www.metoffice.gov.uk/climate_guide/climate/what-affects-climate

3. Barbara Tuchman, *The First Salute: A View of the American Revolution* (New York: Random House, 1989), 254–5.

4. "The Gulf Stream transports nearly four billion cubic feet of water per second, an amount greater than that carried by all of the world's rivers combined." From "How fast is the Gulf Stream?" *National Ocean Service*, National Oceanic and Atmospheric Administration, U.S. Department of Commerce, March 24, 2015 (accessed March 30, 2017), http://oceanservice.noaa.gov/facts/gulfstreamspeed.html.

5. Kerim Hestnes Nisancioglu writes: "Climate fluctuations and changes in our region are closely linked with the heat that is transported from southern latitudes by ocean currents as well as the general wind pattern. Without the Gulf Stream and the westerly winds, Norway would be 10–15C colder." See "The Gulf Stream and ocean heat transport," *Future Learn*, University of Bergen (accessed March 30, 2017), https://www.futurelearn.com/courses/causes-of-climate-change/0/steps/13591.

6. David C. Lund, Jean Lynch-Stieglitz, and William B. Curry, "Gulf Stream Density Structure and Transport during the Past Millennium," *Nature* 444, no. 7119 (November 30, 2006): 601–4, doi:10.1038/nature05277. According to the

International Energy Agency at "Key World Energy Statistics," 2015, accessed June 22, 2017, ftp://ftp.energia.bme.hu/pub/energetikai_alapismeretek/KeyWorld_ Statistics_2015.pdf), yearly world energy consumption is approximately 5.5 x 10^{20} joules [derived from the figure given of 14,000 Mtoe as total world energy consumption in 2013 (page 6) converted to joules by conversion table (page 58)]. Lund gives the heat transport rate as 1.3 x 10^{15} watts. As one watt is one joule per second, the heat transported per year is approximately 3 x 10^{22} watts. This is about 100 times the energy consumed by human civilization.

7. R. Seager, "The source of Europe's mild climate," *American Scientist* 94, no. 4 (2006): 334–341.

8. Geoffrey K. Vallis, *Climate and Oceans* (Princeton, New Jersey: Princeton University Press, 2012), 108.

9. Ibid.

10. Ibid.

11. Tom Garrison, *Oceanography: An Invitation to Marine Science*, 7th ed. (Belmont, CA: Brooks/Cole, Cengage Learning, 2010), 164.

12. "Extreme Temperature Ranges," *50 Degree Temperature Ranges*, National Weather Service, National Oceanic and Atmospheric Administration (accessed March 30, 2017), https://www.weather.gov/ama/50ranges.

13. Vallis, *Climate and Oceans*, chapter 5, section headed, "The Moderating Effect of the Ocean."

14. Ibid.

15. Garrison, *Oceanography*, 164.

16. Cited by Vallis in *Climate and Oceans*, 105; but the attribution is likely apocryphal: see "The Coldest Winter I Ever Spent Was a Summer in San Francisco," *Quote Investigator*, November 30, 2011, accessed June 26, 2017, http://quoteinvestigator. com/2011/11/30/coldest-winter/.

17. Garrison, *Oceanography*, 164.

18. "Water has the highest heat of vaporization per gram of any molecular liquid (2257 J g^{-1} at boiling point)… There is still considerable hydrogen bonding (~75%) in water at 100 °C. As effectively all these bonds need to be broken (very few indeed remaining in the gas phase), there is a great deal of energy required to convert the water to gas, where the water molecules are effectively separated. The increased hydrogen bonding at lower temperatures causes higher heats of vaporization (for example, 44.8 kJ mol^{-1}, at 0 °C)." See Martin Chaplin, "Explanation of the Thermodynamic Anomalies of Water," *Water Structure and Science*, October 14, 2016, accessed March 30, 2017, http://www1.lsbu.ac.uk/water/thermodynamic_anomalies.html#vap; "Fluids – Latent Heat of Evaporation," *The Engineering ToolBox*, accessed March 30, 2017, http://www.engineeringtoolbox.com/fluids-evaporation-latent-heat-d_147. html.

19. "Oxygen – Solubility in Fresh Water and Sea Water," *The Engineering ToolBox* (March 30, 2017), http://www.engineeringtoolbox.com/oxygen-solubility-water-d_841.html.

20. W. Whewell, *Astronomy and General Physics Considered with Reference to Natural Theology* (London: William Pickering, 1834). Available at: https://archive.org/details/astronogenphysics00whewuoft.

21. Ibid., 91–92.

22. Ibid.

23. John M. Wallace and Peter Victor Hobbs, *Atmospheric Science: An Introductory Survey*, 2nd ed., International Geophysics Series 92 (Amsterdam; Boston: Elsevier Academic Press, 2006), see chapter 10.

24. "On the whole, heat has to be moved from the tropics (where the Sun is close to being overhead at noon) to the higher latitudes (where the Sun is 40 degrees off the vertical or lower, on average). These regions, beyond the 40th degree of latitude on either side of the equator, have a heat deficit, while the tropical belt has excess heat. 'Heat deficit' refers to the fact that from these regions more heat is radiated back to space than is received from the Sun, while for the regions with a 'heat excess' the reverse is the case. The climate machine acts as a heat-distributing device; it involves the energy received from the Sun (see 'solar constant'), the energy reflected back to space (see 'albedo') and the energy retained in the atmosphere through the trapping of infrared radiation (see 'greenhouse effect'). If there were no energy transfer the poles would be 25 degrees Celsius cooler, and the equator 14 degrees Celsius warmer!" See "The Earth's Climate Machine," *Climate Change: Earth's Climate System, Climate and Weather*, University of California, San Diego, 2002 (accessed March 30, 2017), http://earthguide.ucsd.edu/virtualmuseum/climatechange1/07_2.shtml.

25. Vallis, *Climate and Oceans*, 123, see chapter 5, section headed "Ocean Heat Transport."

26. Vallis, *Climate and Oceans*; Wallace and Hobbs; Garrison, *Oceanography*, see chapters 8 and 9.

27. Vallis, *Climate and Oceans*, chapter 5; Garrison, *Oceanography*, see chapter 8.

28. Vallis, *Climate and Oceans*, 117, see figure 5.3.

29. "The Earth's Climate Machine," *Climate Change*, http://earthguide.ucsd.edu/virtualmuseum/climatechange1/07_2.shtml.

30. Lawrence Henderson, *The Fitness of the Environment: An Inquiry into the Biological Significance of the Properties of Matter* (New York: The Macmillan Company, 1913), 101–102.

31. F. Laliberté, J. Zika, L. Mudryk, P. J. Kushner, J. Kjellsson, and K. Doos, "Constrained Work Output of the Moist Atmospheric Heat Engine in a Warming Climate," *Science* 347, no. 6221 (January 30, 2015): 540–43, doi:10.1126/science.1257103; T. Schneider, O. P. A. O'Gorman, and X. Levine, "Water Vapor and the Dynamics of Climate Change," *Reviews of Geophysics* 48 (2010), available at https://arxiv.org/pdf/0908.4410; Nick Stokes, "Hadley Cells and Carnot Heat Engine," *moyhu*, February 8, 2015, accessed June 26, 2017, https://moyhu.blogspot.com/2015/02/hadley-cells-and-carnot-heat-engine.html.

32. T. Ose, T. Tokioka, and K. Yamazaki, "Hadley Circulations and Penetrative Cumulus Convection," *Journal of Meteorological Society of Japan* 67, no. 4 (1988): 605–619; Laliberte, Zika, Mudryk, Kushner, Kjellsson, and Doos, "Constrained Work Output of the Moist Atmospheric Heat Engine in a Warming Climate";

Schneider, O'Gorman, and Levine, "Water Vapor and the Dynamics of Climate Change," https://arxiv.org/pdf/0908.4410; Nick Stokes, "Hadley Cells and Carnot Heat Engine," *Moyhu*, February 8, 2015 (accessed March 30, 2017), https://moyhu. blogspot.com/2015/02/hadley-cells-and-carnot-heat-engine.html.

33. Tapio Schneider, Paul A. O'Gorman, Xavier J. Levine, "Water Vapor and the Dynamics of Climate Change," *Reviews of Geophysics* 48, no. 3 (2010).

34. Christopher Minster, "The First New World Voyage of Christopher Columbus (1492)," *ThoughtCo.*, March 30, 2017, accessed June 23, 2017, https://www. thoughtco.com/first-new-world-voyage-christopher-columbus-2136437.

35. Vallis, *Climate and Oceans*, figure 5.3, p. 117; see chapter 5. For an account of the ocean currents see Garrison, *Oceanography*, chapter 9.

36. Garrison, *Oceanography*, see chapter 9.

37. Henderson, *Fitness of the Environment*, 182.

38. Lund, et al., "Gulf Stream Density Structure."

39. Vallis, *Climate and Oceans*, 123.

40. On the question whether it is the downwelling waters which pull the Gulf Stream northward, or the push of the Gulf stream flowing northwards which causes the downwelling, Stefan Rahmstorf writes, "This discussion can be labelled: is the THC pushed or pulled? I.e., pushed by formation of cold deep water, or pulled by downward diffusion of heat through the thermocline? The answer is a question of time scale: ultimately, in the long run, it is pulled. But on shorter time scales, up to centuries, it can be considered pushed in the sense that it is density changes in the deep water formation regions which affect the circulation strength. If this density drops too much so that deep water formation is not possible, the circulation stops. Ultimately, on the long time scale of turbulent mixing, the deep ocean density will drop as well until new deep water formation can start." See Stefan Rahmstorf, "The Thermohaline Ocean Circulation," *Potsdam Institute for Climate Impact Research*, 2006, accessed June 23, 2017, available at http://www.pik-potsdam.de/~stefan/ thc_fact_sheet.html.

41. As I was preparing this chapter, a headline appeared in the *Guardian* newspaper: "Drastic cooling in North Atlantic beyond worst fears, scientists warn." In the article, author Alex Kirby writes: "Current climate models foresee a slowing of the… thermohaline circulation, which is the phenomenon behind the more familiar Gulf Stream that carries warmth from Florida to European shores. If it did slow, that could lead to a dramatic, unprecedented disruption of the climate system." (Alex Kirby, "Drastic cooling in North Atlantic beyond worst fears, scientists warn," *The Guardian*, February 24, 2017 (accessed March 30, 2017), https://www.theguardian. com/environment/2017/feb/24/drastic-cooling-north-atlantic-beyond-worst-fears-scientists-warn. For a contrarian view on this potential threat to the vigor of the Gulf Stream, see Anthony Watts, "URI oceanographer refutes claims that climate change is slowing pace of Gulf Stream," WUWT, March 4, 2015, accessed May 25, 2017, https://wattsupwiththat.com/2014/03/04/uri-oceanographer-refutes-claims-that-climate-change-is-slowing-pace-of-gulf-stream/).

Other research seems to suggest that the Gulf Stream may be much more resistant to weakening. (Anthony Watts, "URI Oceanographer Refutes Claims that Climate Change is Slowing Pace of Gulf Stream," *WUWT*, March 4, 2014, accessed June

5, 2017, available at https://wattsupwiththat.com/2014/03/04/uri-oceanographer-refutes-claims-that-climate-change-is-slowing-pace-of-gulf-stream/)

42. Vivian Montecino and Carina B. Lange, "The Humboldt Current System: Ecosystem Components and Processes, Fisheries, and Sediment Studies," *Progress in Oceanography* 83 (2009): 65–79.

43. G. W. Kling, W. C. Evans, M. L. Tuttle, G. Tanyileke, "Degassing of Lake Nyos," *Nature* 368, no. 6470 (1994): 405–406.

44. W. J. Cromie, *Exploring the Secrets of the Sea* (London: George Allen and Unwin Ltd, 1964), 53.

5. Water, Trees, and Light

1. Carl Sagan, *Cosmos* (New York: Ballantine Books, 2013), 245–255.

2. George Wald, "Life and Light," *Scientific American*, 201, no. 4 (1959): 92–108.

3. See data table in: "Surface Tension," *Wikipedia: The Free Encyclopedia*, The Wikimedia Foundation, June 20, 2017, accessed June 22, 2017, https://en.wikipedia.org/wiki/Surface_tension. Liquid selenium also has a higher surface tension than water, but at a temperature of 217°C; see A. E. Needham, *The Uniqueness of Biological Materials* (Oxford: Pergamon Press, 1965), 11.

4. Lawrence J. Henderson, *The Fitness of the Environment: An Inquiry into the Biological Significance of the Properties of Matter* (New York: The Macmillan Company, 1913), 126–127. Available at https://archive.org/stream/cu31924003093659#page/n145/mode/2up/search/hilgard+.

5. To make a fire sufficiently hot to smelt metals necessitates, as we saw in the previous chapter, the "right fuel." Thin twigs and dried grasses will burn, but such materials are unsuitable for making hot, sustainable fires that can reach high enough temperatures (many hundreds of degrees) to smelt metals from their ores. Wood or wood products such as coal, charcoal, or coke are the only fuels that will do. But this necessitates trees, since without wood there would be no wood, no charcoal, no coal (essentially fossilized wood), and no sustainable fires for smelting metals. Prometheus would be well and truly bound.

The role of surface tension and other unique properties of water in raising water to the top of trees was reviewed in a previous monograph, *Fire-Maker* (Seattle: Discovery Institute Press, 2016), but as it illustrates an important element of fitness of water for life on earth, and specifically terrestrial life, it is appropriate that it is again briefly reviewed here. I take the liberty of abstracting from Chapter 3 of *Fire-Maker* the description of the mechanism involved in the rise of water in trees.

6. Stephen Vogel, *The Life of a Leaf* (Chicago: Chicago University Press, 2010), Chapter 6.

7. N. Michele Holbrook and Maciej A. Zwieniecki, "Transporting Water to the Tops of Trees," *Physics Today* 61 (2008): 76–77.

8. Holbrook and Zwieniecki.

9. Vogel, chapter 6, 93.

10. Holbrook and Zwieniecki.

11. Ibid.

12. Ibid.

13. Melvin T. Tyree, "The Tension Cohesion theory of sap ascent: Current controversies," *Journal of Experimental Botany* 48, no. 315 (1997): 1753–1765.

14. Vogel, 101.

15. Ibid., 91.

16. Holbrook and Zwieniecki.

17. Lignin is an essential component of all plant cell walls and provides the essential element of strength necessary for the construction of tall woody trees. Because it is highly resistant to enzymatic catalysis, its breakdown in the soil is slow, allowing the formation of humus, which retains water and minerals in the soil. See Matti Leisola, Ossi Pastinen, and Douglas D. Axe, "Lignin—Designed Randomness," *BIO-Complexity* 2012 (2012). These properties promoted the growth of large trees and allowed the build-up of vast volumes of undigested vegetation in the Carboniferous swamps, ultimately providing the coal for the steam engines of the early industrial age. Without lignin, there would be no woody plants, no wood, no coal, no charcoal, no fire, no pottery, and certainly no iron and probably no other metals or metallurgy.

18. James C. Forbes, *Plants in Agriculture* (New York: Cambridge University Press, 1992), see figure 4.18, p. 100, and section 4.9.1, "Thermal injury and its avoidance"; Hans Lambers, *Plant Physiological Ecology*, 2nd ed. (New York: Springer, 2008), 225–235.

19. Tim Lenton, *Revolutions That Made the Earth* (New York: Oxford University Press, 2011), chapter 8.

20. Johnjoe McFadden and Jim Al-Khalili, *Life on the Edge: The Coming of Age of Quantum Biology* (New York: Crown Publishers, 2014), chapter 4.

21. See Wald, *Life and Light*, 92–108: "Almost all ordinary ("dark") reactions involve energies of activation between 15 and 65 kilogram calories (kilocalories) per mole. This is equivalent energetically to radiation of wavelengths between 1,900 and 440 millimicrons. [Note: 1 millimicron = 1 nanometer (nm).] The energies required to break single covalent bonds—a process that, through forming free radicals, can be a potent means of chemical activation—almost all fall between 40 and 90 kilocalories per mole, corresponding to radiation of wavelengths 710 to 320 millimicrons. Finally, there is the excitation of valence electrons to higher orbital levels that activates the reactions classified under the heading of photochemistry; this ordinarily involves energies of about 20 to 100 kilocalories per mole, corresponding to the absorption of light of wavelengths 1,430 to 280 millimicrons. Thus, however one approaches the activation of molecules for chemical reactions, one enters into a range of wavelengths that coincides approximately with the photobiological domain... Radiations below 300 millimicrons... are incompatible with the orderly existence of such large, highly organized molecules as proteins and nucleic acids. Both types of molecule consist of long chains of units bound together by primary valences [ordinary chemical bonds]. Both types of molecule, however, are held in their delicate and specific configurations upon which their functions in the cell depend by the relatively weak forces of hydrogen-bonding and van der Waals attraction. These forces, though individually weak, are cumulative. They hold a molecule together in a specific arrangement, like zippers. Radiation of wavelengths shorter than 300 millimicrons unzips them, opening up long sections of attachment, and permitting the orderly arrangement to become random and chaotic. Hence

such radiations denature proteins and depolymerize nucleic acids, with disastrous consequences for the cell. For this reason, about 300 millimicrons represents the lower limit of radiation capable of promoting photoreactions, yet compatible with life."

22. Michael J. Denton, *Nature's Destiny* (New York: Simon and Schuster, 1998), 50–51.

23. Wald.

24. Stephen G. Warren, Richard E. Brandt, and Thomas C. Grenfell, "Visible and Near-Ultraviolet Absorption Spectrum of Ice from Transmission of Solar Radiation into Snow," *Applied Optics* 45, no. 21 (July 20, 2006): 5320. doi:10.1364/AO.45.005320. The authors comment: "The general features of the spectrum are well known… Ice exhibits strong absorption in the ultraviolet (UV) at wavelength 170 nm. With increasing wavelength, the absorption becomes extremely weak in the visible, with a minimum near 400 nm." See Stephen G. Warren and Richard E. Brandt, "Optical Constants of Ice from the Ultraviolet to the Microwave: A Revised Compilation," *Journal of Geophysical Research* 113, no. D14 (July 31, 2008). doi:10.1029/2007JD009744.

25. See Figure 5.4 above; see also *Encyclopedia Britannica*, 15th ed., "Electromagnetic Radiation," *Encyclopaedia Britannica* (Chicago, 1994), figure 3, p. 198.

26. Irina N. Sokolik, "Lecture 7: Absorption spectra of atmospheric gases in the IR, visible and UV regions," *Atmospheric Radiative Transfer*, accessed June 29, 2017, http://irina.eas.gatech.edu/EAS8803_Spring2016/Lec7.pdf.

27. *Encyclopedia Britannica*, 15th ed., "Electromagnetic radiation" (Chicago: Encyclopaedia Britannica, 1994), 203.

28. Warren et al., "Visible and Near-Ultraviolet Absorption Spectrum of Ice from Transmission of Solar Radiation into Snow"; Warren and Brandt, "Optical Constants of Ice from the Ultraviolet to the Microwave: A Revised Compilation."

29. Peter Wadhams, "How Does Arctic Sea Ice Form and Decay?" *PMEL Arctic Zone*, National Oceanic and Atmospheric Administration, United States Department of Commerce, January 1, 2003, accessed March 30, 2017, http://www.pmel.noaa.gov/arctic-zone/essay_wadhams.html.

30. J. C. Loudon, *Encyclopaedia of Gardening* (London: Longman, Hurst, Rees, Orme, Brown, and Green, 1824), 253.

31. William Whewell, *Astronomy and General Physics Considered with Reference to Natural Theology* (London: William Pickering, 1834), 90. Available at: https://archive.org/details/astronogenphysics00whewuoft.

32. Jonathan Lear, *Aristotle: The Desire to Understand* (New York: Cambridge University Press, 1988), 1.

33. Steven A. Benner, Alonso Ricardo, and Matthew A. Carrigan, "Is There a Common Chemical Model for Life in the Universe?" *Current Opinion in Chemical Biology* 8, no. 6 (December 2004): 672–89. On page 686 they comment: "RNA organisms can be much smaller than protein-based organisms… This suggests we might look for RNA organisms on Earth by looking for environments that are space-constrained. Many minerals have pores that are smaller than one micron across. These might hold smaller RNA organisms." See also William Bains, "Many Chemistries Could Be Used to Build Living Systems," *Astrobiology* 4, no. 2 (June 2004): 137–67. doi:10.1089/153110704323175124.

34. Sagan, 102.

6. Water and Human Physiology

1. William Harvey, *Exercitatio Anatomica de Motu Cordis et Sanguinis in Animalibus*, tercentennial edition, trans. Chauncey D. Leake (Springfield, IL and Baltimore, MD: Charles C. Thomas, 1928), 70–71. Available at https://archive.org/stream/exercitatioanato00harv#page/70/mode/2up/search/sun+.

2. David Attenborough, "Human Mammal, Human Hunter," *The Life of Mammals* (BBC, February 5, 2003). Clip available on BBC Earth's YouTube here: https://www.youtube.com/watch?v=826HMLoiE_o. For more information on the series, see "The Life of Mammals," *Wikipedia: The Free Encyclopedia*, The Wikimedia Foundation, November 30, 2016 (accessed March 30, 2017), https://en.wikipedia.org/wiki/The_Life_of_Mammals.

3. D. Lieberman, D. M. Bramble, D. A. Raichlen, and J. J. Shea, "Brains, Brawn, and the Evolution of Human Endurance Running Capabilities," in *The First Humans: Origin and Early Evolution of the Genus Homo: Contributions from the Third Stony Brook Human Evolution Symposium and Workshop, October 3–October 7, 2006*, edited by Frederick E. Grine, John G. Fleagle, and Richard E. Leakey, Vertebrate Paleobiology and Paleoanthropology Series (Dordrecht: Springer, 2009), 77–92; see page 85.

4. Ibid., 77.

5. Ibid., 85.

6. Knut Schmidt-Nielsen, *Animal Physiology: Adaptation and Environment*, 5th ed. (New York: Cambridge University Press, 1997), chapter 7, page 252, in section headed "Evaporation."

7. Lawrence Henderson, *The Fitness of the Environment: An Inquiry into the Biological Significance of the Properties of Matter* (New York: The Macmillan Company, 1913), 80–91; A. E. Needham, *The Uniqueness of Biological Materials* (Oxford: Pergamon Press, 1965), 98.

8. Needham, 13.

9. "Water – Thermodynamic Properties," *The Engineering ToolBox* (accessed March 30, 2017), http://www.engineeringtoolbox.com/water-thermal-properties-d_162.html; "Sodium," *Wikipedia: The Free Encyclopedia*, The Wikimedia Foundation, March 30, 2017 (accessed March 30, 2017), https://en.wikipedia.org/wiki/Sodium; "Mercury (element)," *Wikipedia: The Free Encyclopedia*, The Wikimedia Foundation, March 26, 2017 (accessed March 30, 2017), https://en.wikipedia.org/wiki/Mercury_(element).

10. "Water has the highest heat of vaporization per gram of any molecular liquid (2257 J g^{-1} at boiling point)... There is still considerable hydrogen bonding (~75%) in water at 100 °C. As effectively all these bonds need to be broken (very few indeed remaining in the gas phase), there is a great deal of energy required to convert the water to gas, where the water molecules are effectively separated. The increased hydrogen bonding at lower temperatures causes higher heats of vaporization (for example, 44.8 kJ mol^{-1}, at 0 °C)." Martin Chaplin, "Explanation of the Thermodynamic Anomalies of Water (T1–T11)," *Water Structure and Science*, October 14, 2016 (accessed March 30, 2017), http://www1.lsbu.ac.uk/water/thermodynamic_anomalies.html#vap;

"Fluids – Latent Heat of Evaporation," *The Engineering ToolBox* (accessed March 30, 2017), http://www.engineeringtoolbox.com/fluids-evaporation-latent-heat-d_147.html.

11. Eugene F. Du Bois, "Heat Loss from the Human Body," Harvey Lecture, December 15, 1938, available at https://www.ncbi.nlm.nih.gov/pmc/articles/PMC1911367/pdf/bullnyacadmed00588-0016.pdf; Henderson, 102–103; Schmidt-Nielsen, chapter 7, fig. 7.21.

12. Du Bois; Henderson, 102–103; Schmidt-Nielsen, chapter 7, fig. 7.21.

13. Schmidt-Nielsen (1997) chapter 7, page 253, in section entitled "Evaporation."

14. Du Bois; Henderson, 102–103; Schmidt-Nielsen, chapter 7.

15. A good account of the physics of heat transfer and temperature regulation as it applies to biological systems, including the roles of radiation and conduction, is given in Knut Schmidt-Nielsen's *Animal Physiology*, chapter 7.

16. Henderson, 102–103.

17. N. R. Pace, "A Molecular View of Microbial Diversity and the Biosphere," *Science* 276, no. 5313 (May 2, 1997): 734–40. doi:10.1126/science.276.5313.734.

18. Mayo Clinic Staff, "Anhidrosis," *Mayo Clinic*, Mayo Foundation for Medical Education and Research, December 13, 2014 (accessed March 30, 2017), http://www.mayoclinic.org/diseases-conditions/anhidrosis/basics/definition/con-20033498.

19. One might wonder what the point of being a warm-blooded homeotherm is, given its need to maintain its body temperature at a fairly constant level. The advantages are evident in many different lineages that have achieved and maintained warm-bloodedness over millions of years. Almost all mammals and birds are warm-blooded homeotherms (with very few exceptions, such as the mole rat, and in unusual circumstances like hibernating). These two groups include the most active and intelligent animals on Earth. Homeothermy allows constant activity in a wider range of environmental temperatures. Warm-blooded animals thrive in the frigid polar regions (penguins) and in the hottest deserts (camels). Warm-bloodedness increases the rates of metabolic activity, which provides many physiological benefits. So, for example, even some predatory "cold-blooded" fish maintain their eyes and nervous systems at a higher temperature than the rest of their bodies to improve the efficiency of vision.

20. Needham, 13; Henderson, 81. Also, from http://www1.lsbu.ac.uk/water/thermodynamic_anomalies.html#vap: Water has the highest specific heat of all liquids except ammonia. The values for C_V and C_p are 4.1375 J g^{-1} K^{-1} and 4.1819 J g^{-1} K1 at 25°C respectively (compare C_p pentane 1.66 J g^{-1} K^{-1}). As water is heated, the increased movement of water causes the hydrogen bonds to bend and break. As the energy absorbed in these processes is not available to increase the kinetic energy of the water, it takes considerable heat to raise water's temperature. Also, as water is a light molecule there are more molecules per gram than in most similar molecules to absorb this energy. Heat absorbed is given out on cooling, thus allowing water to act as a heat reservoir, buffering against changes in temperature. Thus, the water in our oceans stores vast amounts of energy, and in this way moderates Earth's climate. http://www.engineeringtoolbox.com/specific-heat-capacity-d_391.html.

21. Garrison, *Oceanography*, 163.

22. Henderson, 89.

23. Henderson, 90.

24. NatureNorth, "Shivering to Warm Flight Muscles," August 26, 2013, YouTube video (0:29), https://www.youtube.com/watch?v=8Ta-O8cEoTQ.

25. C. D. Bramwell and P. B. Fellgett, "Thermal regulation in sail lizards," *Nature* 242 (1973): 203–205. doi:10.1038/242203a0.

26. Martin Chaplin, "Explanation of the Thermodynamic Anomalies of Water (T1–T11)," *Water Structure and Science*, October 14, 2016 (accessed March 30, 2017), http://www1.lsbu.ac.uk/water/thermodynamic_anomalies.html#Cpminp.

27. Schmidt-Nielsen (1997), chapter 7, see table 7.3.

28. Schmidt-Nielsen (1997); Needham, 22; "Thermal Conductivity of Common Materials and Gases," *The Engineering ToolBox* (accessed March 30, 2017), http://www.engineeringtoolbox.com/thermal-conductivity-d_429.html.

29. Ibid. The authors comment: "Apart from liquid metals, water has the highest thermal conductivity of any liquid. For most liquids the thermal conductivity (the rate at which energy is transferred down a temperature gradient) falls with increasing temperature but this occurs only above about 130°C in liquid water." From Chaplin, "Explanation of the Thermodynamic Anomalies of Water (T1–T11)," http://www1.lsbu.ac.uk/water/thermodynamic_anomalies.html#cond.

30. Henderson, 106; Needham, 22.

31. Chaplin, "Explanation of the Thermodynamic Anomalies of Water (T1–T11)," http://www1.lsbu.ac.uk/water/thermodynamic_anomalies.html#cond.

32. "Ammonia—NH_3—Thermodynamic Properties," *The Engineering ToolBox* (accessed March 30, 2017), http://www.engineeringtoolbox.com/ammonia-d_971.html; "Water—Thermodynamic Properties," *The Engineering ToolBox*, http://www.engineeringtoolbox.com/water-thermal-properties-d_162.html.

33. "Water—Thermodynamic Properties," *The Engineering ToolBox*, http://www.engineeringtoolbox.com/water-thermal-properties-d_162.html; "Sodium," *Wikipedia: The Free Encyclopedia*, https://en.wikipedia.org/wiki/Sodium; "Mercury (element)," *Wikipedia: The Free Encyclopedia*, https://en.wikipedia.org/wiki/Mercury_(element).

34. L. J. Rothschild and R. L. Mancinelli, "Life in Extreme Environments," *Nature* 409, no. 6823 (February 22, 2001): 1092–1101. doi:10.1038/35059215.

35. *Convection* is a quite different heat-transfer mechanism from conduction, involving the bulk movement of gases and fluids. Heat is absorbed by some substance, generally a gas or fluid, which then "moves," carrying the heat from the source of absorption to another site where the heat is given off. Convection is heat transference by movement. Unlike conduction, convection is an efficient mechanism for transporting heat rapidly over much longer distances. Heat transference by convection is utilized in a blow-heater or a fan to redistribute or circulate heat within a room. Central heating systems which pump heated water through pipes exploit convection to redistribute heat in the same way as the circulatory system in the body.

36. Schmidt-Nielsen, appendix B.

37. Ibid., 585.

38. Ibid., chapter 1, 50–61.

39. Steven Vogel, *Comparative Biomechanics: Life's Physical World*, (Princeton, NJ: Princeton University Press, 2013), chapter 10.

40. Henderson, 68 and 116.

41. "Isothermal Compressibility of Liquids," *Handbook of Tables for Applied Engineering Science*, The University of Iowa College of Engineering (accessed March 30, 2017), http://www.engineering.uiowa.edu/~cfd/pdfs/tables/1-42B.pdf; Y. Marcus and G. T. Hefter, "The Compressibility of Liquids at Ambient Temperature and Pressure," *Journal of Molecular Liquids* 73–74 (November 1997): 61–74. doi:10.1016/S0167-7322(97)00057-3.

42. "Viscosity," *Wikipedia: The Free Encyclopedia*, https://en.wikipedia.org/wiki/Viscosity; "Absolute, Dynamic and Kinematic Viscosity," *The Engineering ToolBox* (accessed March 30, 2017), http://www.engineeringtoolbox.com/dynamic-absolute-kinematic-viscosity-d_412.html.

43. "Viscosity," *Wikipedia: The Free Encyclopedia*, https://en.wikipedia.org/wiki/Viscosity.

44. Vogel, *Comparative Biomechanics*, chapter 9; Schmidt-Nielsen, see chapter 3, section headed "Viscosity."

45. Vogel, *Comparative Biomechanics*, chapter 10, 186, states that powering the circulatory system uses up 10.7 percent of resting metabolic rate. Other sources imply similar percentages. See "Which of these parts of the human body uses more oxygen: the lungs, heart or brain?" *Quora*, March 2, 2016 (accessed March 30, 2017), https://www.quora.com/Which-of-these-parts-of-the-human-body-uses-more-oxygen-the-lungs-heart-or-brain; see chart which indicates that the heart uses up about 10 % of total oxygen consumption of the body; and see R. E. Klabunde, "Myocardial Oxygen Demand," *Cardiovascular Physiology Concepts*, April 2, 2007 (accessed March 30, 2017), at http://www.cvphysiology.com/CAD/CAD003, which gives resting heart O_2 consumption as 24 ml O_2/min assuming a heart mass of 300 grams. The total oxygen consumption of the body at rest is 250 ml per minute; see J. N. Maina, "Comparative Respiratory Morphology: Themes and Principles in the Design and Construction of the Gas Exchangers," *The Anatomical Record* 261, no. 1 (February 15, 2000): 25–44.

46. Schmidt-Nielsen, 112.

47. Ibid.

48. Vogel, *Comparative Biomechanics*, chapter 10; see section matching diffusion and convection, 187.

49. Ibid., chapter 9, 164.

50. For a more detailed discussion of the Hagen-Poiseuille equation and the implication for circulatory design see Vogel, *Comparative Biomechanics*, chapters 9 and 10.

51. Michael J. Denton, "The Place of Life and Man in Nature: Defending the Anthropocentric Thesis," *BIO-Complexity* 2013, no. 1 (February 25, 2013). doi:10.5048/BIO-C.2013.1.

52. Vogel, *Comparative Biomechanics*, chapter 6, p. 93.

53. Carol Porth, ed., *Essentials of Pathophysiology: Concepts of Altered Health States* (Philadelphia: Wolters Kluwer/Lippincott Williams & Wilkins, 2011), 380.

54. Ibid., 381.

55. Ibid., 416.

56. R. E. Klabunde, "Turbulent Flow," *Cardiovascular Physiology Concepts*, April 10, 2007, accessed June 1, 2017, http://www.cvphysiology.com/Hemodynamics/H007.htm.

57. Paul Clements and Carl Gwinnutt, "The Physics of Flow," *Anaesthesia UK*, 2016, http://www.frca.co.uk/Documents/100308%20Physics%20of%20flowLR.pdf.

58. Ibid.

59. Vogel, *Comparative Biomechanics*, see discussion in chapter 10, 189–193, of Murray's Law and the relationship between shear stress and remodeling of arterial walls; see also T. F. Sherman, "On Connecting Large Vessels to Small: The Meaning of Murray's Law," J Gen Physiology 78 (Oct 1981): 431–453.

60. Vogel, *Comparative Biomechanics*, chapter 10, 187.

61. C. D. Murray, "The Physiological Principle of Minimum Work: I. The Vascular System and the Cost of Blood Volume," *PNAS USA* 12 (Mar 1926): 207–214.

62. For a more quantitative discussion and review of this area, see Vogel's *Comparative Biomechanics*, chapter 10, and Schmidt-Nielsen's *Animal Physiology*, chapter 3.

63. David C. Catling, Christopher R. Glein, Kevin J. Zahnle, and Christopher P. McKay, "Why O2 Is Required by Complex Life on Habitable Planets and the Concept of Planetary 'Oxygenation Time,'" *Astrobiology* 5, no. 3 (June 2005): 415–38, doi:10.1089/ast.2005.5.415; Wald, "The Origin of Life."

64. "Animal Fact Sheet: Merriam's Kangaroo Rat," *Arizona-Sonora Desert Museum*, 2017 (accessed March 30, 2017), http://www.desertmuseum.org/kids/oz/long-fact-sheets/krat.php.

65. M. Lieberman and A. D. Marks, *Marks' Basic Medical Biochemistry: A Clinical Approach*, 3rd North American ed. (Philadelphia: Lippincott Williams & Wilkins, 2008); see pages 46–53 for discussion of buffers and the bicarbonate buffer.

66. Ibid., 50–51.

67. B. D. Rose, *Clinical Physiology of Acid-Base and Electrolyte Disorders* (New York: McGraw-Hill, 1977), 176.

68. The production of acids and the consequent generation of H+ ions are an inevitable result of the oxidative metabolism of organic compounds, because many of the intermediates on the path from sugar to CO_2 are acids. In fact, the first part of the main catabolic pathway involves oxidative rearrangements in the intermediary compounds which can occur in the absence of oxygen, and when an organism is deprived of oxygen for any length of time, a considerable build-up of acid is bound to occur. Some organisms derive all their energy from this first part of the catabolic pathway; indeed, catabolism in the absence of oxygen, known as anaerobic metabolism, is vital even in organisms such as mammals which derive most of their energy from the complete oxidative catabolism of carbon to H_2O and CO_2. Moreover, as Henderson points out (158): "In the main the foodstuffs are neutral substances, but their principal end products, except water, are almost exclusively acid compounds—carbonic acid, phosphoric acid, sulphuric acid, uric acid."

69. Fish blood contains less bicarbonate than mammalian blood. Why? This is explained in D. H. Evans and J. B. Claiborne, eds., *The Physiology of Fishes*, 2nd ed. (Boca Raton, FL: CRC Press, 1997), 177–198. As the authors point out, fish must

maintain high rates of water flow across the gills to obtain sufficient oxygen for their metabolic needs, and as the level of CO_2 in natural bodies of water is low, the blood CO_2 levels in fish are much lower than in a mammal (where the blood is exposed in the lungs to relatively high pCO_2 levels). Consequently, as they comment: "plasma CO_2 levels are depressed well below mammalian values, and at physiological pH values [HCO_3] must be lower as well... a 2 mm Hg increase in fish pCO_2 will... change the pH by 0.18 units... a fifty % increase in [H^+]. This same absolute pCO change in humans results in only a negligible 0.01 units; approximately 2% pH alteration."

70. Henderson, chapter 4, 153.

71. J. T. Edsall and J. Wyman, *Biophysical Chemistry*, vol. 1 (New York: Academic Press, 1958), 550. Every detail of this buffer system reveals further aspects to its fitness. For example, take the actual process of hydration itself, described by Edsall and Wyman, 554: "[T]he hydration of CO_2 to H_2CO_3 is a process requiring a rearrangement of the valence bonds, the two C—O bonds of CO_2, 180° apart and 1.15 Å long, being transformed to the three C—O bonds of H_2CO_3, approximately 120° apart and not far from 1.3 Å long. We shall not attempt to comment here on the details of the electronic rearrangements that must be involved in the process, and indeed little is known of them. It is not surprising, however, that a process such as this should require an appreciable time, in contrast for example to such a process as the hydration of NH_3 to NH_4OH in which the hydration process simply involves the formation of a hydrogen bond between the unshared electron pair in the ammonia molecule." This apparently esoteric point, the slowness of the hydration of CO_2, may be of considerable physiological importance. Hydration is much slower in the blood than in the red cell, which possesses the enzyme carbonic anhydrase. If hydration were instantaneous, this would mean that whenever CO_2 levels in the blood or body tissues increased suddenly following some respiratory distress, this might well provoke a lethal acidosis.

72. Iain Johnston pointed out in a personal communication, "The ventilatory control centre in the brainstem is exquisitely sensitive to bloodstream CO_2 concentration, with a minute by minute response sensitive output, increasing both tidal volumes and respiratory rates very rapidly to rising CO_2 concentrations."

73. J. N. Maina, "Structure and function and evolution of the gas exchangers: Comparative perspectives," *Journal of Anatomy* 201(2002): 281–304.

74. Jean-Jacques Hublin, Abdelouahed Ben-Ncer, Shara E. Bailey, Sarah E. Freidline, Simon Neubauer, Matthew M. Skinner, Inga Bergmann, et al., "New Fossils from Jebel Irhoud, Morocco and the Pan-African Origin of Homo Sapiens," *Nature* 546, no. 7657 (June 7, 2017): 289–92. doi:10.1038/nature22336.

75. Steve Drury, "Out of Africa: A Little Less Blurred?" *earth-pages*, September 25, 3016, accessed June 22, 2017, https://earth-pages.co.uk/tag/out-of-africa/.

7. Water and the Cell

1. Philip Ball, "Water as an Active Constituent in Cell Biology," *Chemical Reviews* 108, no. 1 (2008): 74–108.

2. Anders Nilsson and Lars G. M. Pettersson, "The Structural Origin of Anomalous Properties of Liquid Water," *Nature Communications* 6 (December 8, 2015): 8998. doi:10.1038/ncomms9998.

3. L. J. Rothschild and R. L. Mancinelli, "Life in Extreme Environments," *Nature* 409, no. 6823 (February 22, 2001): 1092–1101, doi:10.1038/35059215; Juliette Ravaux, Gérard Hamel, Magali Zbinden, Aurélie A. Tasiemski, Isabelle Boutet, Nelly Léger, Arnaud Tanguy, Didier Jollivet, and Bruce Shillito, "Thermal Limit for Metazoan Life in Question: In Vivo Heat Tolerance of the Pompeii Worm," *PloS One* 8, no. 5 (2013): e64074, doi:10.1371/journal.pone.0064074.

4. Ravaux, Hamel, et al., op. cit.

5. W. J. Gehring and R. Wehner, "Heat Shock Protein Synthesis and Thermotolerance in Cataglyphis, an Ant from the Sahara Desert," *Proceedings of the National Academy of Sciences of the United States of America* 92, no. 7 (March 28, 1995): 2994–98.

6. David Attenborough, *Africa*, Episode 5: "Sahara," BBC.

7. Rothschild and Mancinelli, 1092–1101.

8. Ken Takai, Kentaro Nakamura, Tomohiro Toki, Urumu Tsunogai, Masayuki Miyazaki, Junichi Miyazaki, Hisako Hirayama, Satoshi Nakagawa, Takuro Nunoura, and Koki Horikoshi, "Cell Proliferation at 122 Degrees C and Isotopically Heavy CH4 Production by a Hyperthermophilic Methanogen under High-Pressure Cultivation," *Proceedings of the National Academy of Sciences of the United States of America* 105, no. 31 (August 5, 2008): 10949–54. doi:10.1073/pnas.0712334105.

9. Bruce M. Jakosky, Kenneth H. Nealson, Corien Bakermans, Ruth E. Ley, and Michael T. Mellon, "Subfreezing Activity of Microorganisms and the Potential Habitability of Mars' Polar Regions," *Astrobiology* 3, no. 2 (June 2003): 343–50. doi:10.1089/153110703769016433.

10. Rothschild and Mancinelli.

11. Andrew Clarke, G. John Morris, Fernanda Fonseca, Benjamin J. Murray, Elizabeth Acton, and Hannah C. Price, "A Low Temperature Limit for Life on Earth," *PloS One* 8, no. 6 (2013): e66207. doi:10.1371/journal.pone.0066207.

12. Ibid.

13. In *Nature's Destiny* (p. 111), I wrote: "Even a temperature change of far less than 100°C causes a quite dramatic slowing of reaction times. Reactions occurring in the human body at 38°C would take place 16 times slower at 0°C and 64 times slower at −20°C. As Robert E. D. Clark points out, at temperatures below −100°C all chemical reactions become vanishingly slow and at the temperature of liquid air [i.e., about −200°C], 'only a few reactions take place at all, and these involve the exceedingly active element fluorine in its free state.'" See Clark's *The Universe: Plan or Accident?* (London: Paternoster Press, 1961), 59.

14. George Wald, "The Origins of Life," *Proceedings of the National Academy of Science US* 52 (1964): 594–611.

15. I. B. Johns, E. A. McElhill, and J. O. Smith, "Thermal Stability of Organic Compounds," *Industrial & Engineering Chemistry Product Research and Development* 1, no. 1 (March 1, 1962): 2–6. doi:10.1021/i360001a001. The authors comment: "The finite strength of chemical bonds puts an upper limit on the vibrational energy that molecules may possess without bond rupture. Most organic compounds are

limited in stability by having in their structures pathways for rearrangements of the atoms at temperatures far below the temperatures required for straightforward bond rupture."

16. Isaac Asimov, *The World of Carbon* (New York: Collier Books, 1962), 11–12.

17. S. L. Miller, and L. E. Orgel, *The Origins of Life on the Earth* (New Jersey: Prentice Hall, 1974). See chapter 9 on the stability of organic compounds.

18. Ibid.

19. H. R. White, "Hydrolytic stability of biomolecules at high temperatures and its implication for life at 250°C," *Nature* 310 (1984): 430–432. See also H. Bernhardt, D. Ludeman, and R. Jaenicke, "Biomolecules are Unstable under Black Smoker Conditions," *Naturwissenchaften* 71 (1984): 583–586.

20. White, (1984): 430–432. See also Bernhardt, Ludeman, and Jaenicke, 583–586.

21. See A. Michelle Caldwell, "What Happens When Sucrose Is Heated?" *eHow* (accessed March 31, 2017), http://www.ehow.com/facts_6002499_happens-sucrose-heated_.html; "Sugar doesn't melt – it decomposes, scientists demonstrate," *Science Daily*, August 2, 2011 (accessed June 6, 2017), https://www.sciencedaily.com/releases/2011/07/110725123549.htm; "The why, how and consequences of cooking our food," *Eufic*, November 8, 2010 (accessed March 31, 2017), http://www.eufic.org/article/en/expid/cooking-review-eufic/.

22. Lawrence Henderson, *The Fitness of the Environment: An Inquiry into the Biological Significance of the Properties of Matter* (New York: The Macmillan Company, 1913), 220.

23. J. B. S. Haldane referred to this characteristic 'metastability' in a symposium some time ago [J. B. S. Haldane, "The Origin of Life," *New Biology* 16 (1954): 12 –27]. He defined a metastable molecule as one that can liberate free energy by a transformation, but is stable enough to last a long time unless it is activated by heat, radiation, or union with a catalyst. He cited trinitrotoluene as an example of a highly metastable molecule. As he pointed out, a kilogram of it liberates a lot of energy. Glucose, on the other hand, is only mildly metastable, but will liberate some energy if turned into ethanol and carbon dioxide. As he states, most organic molecules are metastable. A. E. Needham, in *The Uniqueness of Biological Materials* (Oxford: Pergamon Press, 1965), refers to Haldane's description of organics as 'metastable' on page 30.

24. Needham, 30–33.

25. Michael Denton, *Nature's Destiny* (New York: The Free Press, 1998), p. 110: "The softening of meat occurs because the collagen fibers which make up the tendons and fibrous sheets are converted [decomposed into] into soft gelatin, which offers no resistance to a knife. When sugars are heated above 100°C, they are rapidly degraded, undergoing complex chemical reactions with themselves and other biomolecules in the food. These changes are referred to as caramelization and browning in the kitchen." See also Laurent Bozec and Marianne Odlyha, "Thermal Denaturation Studies of Collagen by Microthermal Analysis and Atomic Force Microscopy," *Biophysical Journal* 101, no. 1 (July 2011): 228–236. doi:10.1016/j.bpj.2011.04.033.

26. For the requirement for a liquid matrix [water in the case of Terran life] see: J. A. Baross, S. A. Benner, et al., *The Limits of Organic Life in Planetary Systems*

(Washington, DC: National Academies Press, 2007), p. 1; Louis N. Irwin, *Cosmic Biology: How Life Could Evolve on Other Worlds* (New York; London: Springer-Praxis Books in Popular Astronomy, 2011), 32, 43; Kevin W. Plaxco, *Astrobiology: A Brief Introduction*, 2nd ed. (Baltimore: Johns Hopkins University Press, 2011), 7–8; Needham, 9; Louis Neal Irwin and Dirk Schulze-Makuch, *Cosmic Biology: How Life Could Evolve on Other Worlds*, Springer-Praxis Books in Popular Astronomy (New York, London, Chichester: Springer/Praxis, 2011). The authors of the last-cited work find the necessity for a liquid matrix "compelling" (p. 43) and claim that liquids provide "overwhelming advantages" (p. 32) over solids and gases to serve as the matrix of life.

27. See Needham, 9–10.

28. Luke Mastin, "Timeline of the Big Bang," *The Physics of the Universe*, 2009 (accessed March 31, 2017), http://www.physicsoftheuniverse.com/topics_bigbang_timeline.html. The Planck temperature is 1.41×10^{32}K.

29. F. Hoyle, "Ultrahigh Temperatures," *Scientific American* 191, no. 3 (1954): 145–154.

30. Dedra Forbes, "Temperature at the Center of the Sun," *The Physics Factbook: An encyclopedia of scientific essays*, Glenn Elert ed., 1997 (accessed March 31, 2017), http://hypertextbook.com/facts/1997/DedraForbes.shtml.

31. "Stellar Spectral Types," *HyperPhysics*, Georgia State University College of Arts and Sciences, August 2000 (accessed March 31, 2017), http://hyperphysics.phy-astr.gsu.edu/hbase/Starlog/staspe.html.

32. Glenn Elert, "Viscosity," *The Physics Hypertextbook*, 2017, accessed June 26, 2017, http://physics.info/viscosity/; for viscosity of crustal rocks see: Yaolin Shi, and Jianling Cao, "Lithosphere Effective Viscosity of Continental China," *Earth Science Frontiers* 15, no. 3 (May 2008): 82–95. doi:10.1016/S1872-5791(08)60064-0.

33. "Oxygen – Solubility in Fresh Water and Sea Water," *The Engineering ToolBox* (accessed March 31, 2017), http://www.engineeringtoolbox.com/oxygen-solubility-water-d_841.html.

34. Needham, 16.

35. Alok Jha, *The Water Book* (London: Headline, 2015), 20.

36. "Maximum Moisture Carrying Capacity of Air," *The Engineering ToolBox* (accessed March 31, 2017), http://www.engineeringtoolbox.com/maximum-moisture-content-air-d_1403.html.

37. For a complete list of all the anomalous properties of water see Martin Chaplin, "Anomalous properties of water," *Water Structure and Science*, March 28, 2017 (accessed March 31, 2017), http://www1.lsbu.ac.uk/water/water_anomalies.html.

38. Henderson; John T. Edsall, *Biophysical Chemistry: Thermodynamics, Electrostatics, and the Biological Significance of the Properties of Matter* (New York: Academic Press, 1958); Needham; Philip Ball, H_2O: *A Biography of Water* (London: Weidenfeld and Nicolson, 1999).

39. Philip Ball, "Why Water Is Weird," a talk presented at the Royal Society of Chemistry, April 2011, available at http://www.philipball.co.uk/articles/water.

40. Jha, 24.

41. F. Franks, "Water: the Unique Chemical," in *Water: A Comprehensive Treatise*, vol. 1 (New York: Plenum Press, 1972), 20.

42. For a good overview of the concept and its history, see "Alkahest," *Wikipedia: The Free Encyclopedia*, The Wikimedia Foundation, February 8, 2017 (accessed March 31, 2017), https://en.wikipedia.org/wiki/Alkahest.

43. Henderson, 111.

44. See Ball, "Water as an Active Constituent in Cell Biology."

45. Ibid.

46. Jane B. Reece and Neil A. Campbell, eds., *Campbell Biology*, 9th ed. (Boston: Benjamin Cummings/Pearson, 2011), 46.

47. Ball, "Water as an Active Constituent in Cell Biology."

48. Charles Tanford, "How Protein Chemists Learned about the Hydrophobic Factor," *Protein Science* 6, no. 6 (June 1997): 1358–66. doi:10.1002/pro.5560060627.

49. Dongdong Jia, Jonathan Hamilton, Lenu M. Zaman, and Anura Goonewardene, "The Time, Size, Viscosity, and Temperature Dependence of the Brownian Motion of Polystyrene Microspheres," *American Journal of Physics* 75, no. 2 (February 2007): 111–15. doi:10.1119/1.2386163.

50. Knut Schmidt-Nielsen, *Animal Physiology: Adaptation and Environment*, 5th ed. (Cambridge and New York: Cambridge University Press, 1997), Appendix B, 587.

51. In passing it is worth noting that the structure of intracellular water is the subject of considerable controversy. See: K. Luby–Phelps, "Cytoarchitecture and Physical Properties of Cytoplasm: Volume Viscosity, Diffusion, Intracellular Surface Area," *International Review of Cytology* 192 (2000): 189–221; G. H. Pollack and F. B. Reitz, "Phase transitions and molecular motion in the cell," *Cell. Mol. Biol.* 47 (2001): 885–900; G. H. Pollack, *Cells, Gels, and the Engines of Life* (Seattle: Ebner & Sons, 2001); Ball, "Water as an Active Constituent in Cell Biology"; Martin Chaplin, "The Importance of Cell Water," *Science in Society Archive*, October 4, 2013 (accessed March 31, 2017), http://www.i-sis.org.uk/TIOCW.php; Martin Chaplin, "Do We Underestimate the Importance of Water in Cell Biology?" *Nature Reviews, Molecular Cell Biology* 7, no. 11 (November 2006): 861–66, doi:10.1038/nrm2021. Boris Zaslavsky notes that water beside most (solid) interfaces possesses "significantly different properties from those of the respective bulk systems. The term vicinal water was suggested by Drost-Hansen… for such interfacial water…. [V]icinal water is water the structure of which is modified by proximity to an interface but excluding chemically 'bound' water directly on the surface (the water of primary hydration)." See Boris Y. Zaslavsky, *Aqueous Two-Phase Partitioning: Physical Chemistry and Bioanalytical Applications* (New York: M. Dekker, 1995), 50. Although most authors accept the existence of vicinal water in the cell and that it consists of a series of hydrogen-bonded layers, and that its properties differ from ordinary bulk water, just how much of the intracellular water is highly structured vicinal, and how much bulk, is subject to debate. Many recent attempts to measure intracellular viscosity show that the viscosity of at least a substantial percentage is not so different from bulk water. See Erik Persson and Bertil Halle, "Cell Water Dynamics on Multiple Time Scales," *Proceedings of the National Academy of Sciences of the United States of America* 105, no. 17 (April 29, 2008): 6266–71. doi:10.1073/pnas.0709585105.

52. Jha, 115–116.

53. Nick Lane, *The Vital Question: Energy, Evolution, and the Origins of Complex Life* (London: Profile Books, 2015), 13.

54. Harold Morowitz, *Cosmic Joy and Local Pain: Musing of a Mystic Scientist* (New York: Scribner, 1987), 152–153.

55. Albert Szent-Györgyi, *The Living State: With Observations on Cancer* (New York: Academic Press, 1972), 9.

56. Ball, "Water as an Active Constituent in Cell Biology."

57. Ibid.

58. Ibid.

59. Gerald H. Pollack, Ivan L. Cameron, and D. N. Wheatley, eds., *Water and the Cell* (Dordrecht: Springer, 2006), preface, viii.

60. Gilbert Ling, "A Convergence of Experimental and Theoretical Breakthroughs Affirms the PM Theory of Dynamically Structured Cell Water on the Theory's 40th Birthday," in the above-cited *Water and the Cell*; Pollack, *Cells, Gels and the Engines of Life: A New, Unifying Approach to Cell Function.*

61. Ball, "Water as an Active Constituent in Cell Biology."

62. See Pollack, *Cells, Gels, and the Engine of Life*: "Evidence for a crucial difference between the organization of water molecules in bulk water and in the cell is provided by… resistance to water loss in desert plants facing months without rainfall; immunity to freezing in arctic regions; and the cell's ability to remain intact even when dismembered" (p. 73). Pollack further notes: "In Seattle the damp winter gloom coupled with a ready made source of wood inspired frequent fire place activity. Seasoned wood burns well, but everyone knows that wet wood merely sizzles. The surprise is that seasoning can require a year—even for split logs. Water clings tenaciously. Such tenacity is not ever seen in logs whose molecular structure has deteriorated from age. Old wood dumped into a water tub until saturated will dry in short order. Thus, the water-adsorptive force lies in nature's surface design. The force is strong enough to resist all but fanatical attempts at dehydration" (page 271).

8. Conclusion

1. Loren C. Eiseley, *The Immense Journey* (New York: Vintage Books, 1973), 161–162. Available at: http://books.google.com/books?id=NaxJAAAAMAAJ.

2. William Blake, "Auguries of Innocence," available at *Poetry Foundation*, accessed June 6, 2017, https://www.poetryfoundation.org/poems-and-poets/poems/detail/43650.

3. "Far away in the heavenly abode of the great god Indra, there is a wonderful net which has been hung by some cunning artificer in such a manner that it stretches out infinitely in all directions. In accordance with the extravagant tastes of deities, the artificer has hung a single glittering jewel in each 'eye' of the net, and since the net itself is infinite in dimension, the jewels are infinite in number… If we now arbitrarily select one of these jewels for inspection… we will discover that in its polished surface there are reflected *all* the other jewels in the net, infinite in number. Not only that, but each of the jewels reflected in this one jewel is also reflecting all the other jewels." Francis Harold Cook, *Hua-Yen Buddhism: The Jewel Net of Indra* (University Park and London: The Pennsylvania State University Press, 1977), 2.

4. F. Hoyle, "The Universe: Past and Present Reflections," *Engineering and Science*, November 1981. Available at: http://calteches.library.caltech.edu/527/2/Hoyle.pdf.

5. Andrew Clarke, G. John Morris, Fernanda Fonseca, Benjamin J. Murray, Elizabeth Acton, and Hannah C. Price, "A Low Temperature Limit for Life on Earth," *PloS One* 8, no. 6 (2013): e66207. doi:10.1371/journal.pone.0066207.

6. J. A. Baross, S. A. Benner, et al., *The Limits of Organic Life in Planetary Systems* (Washington, D.C.: National Academies Press, 2007). On the reactivity of water, see pp. 27, 70; on water as an alleged obstacle to the origin of life, see pp. 58–61.

7. Philip Ball, "Will ET Drink Water?" *Cosmos, Nautilus,* November 2016, accessed June 2, 2017, http://cosmos.nautil.us/feature/21/will-et-.

8. Nick Lane, *The Vital Question: Energy, Evolution, and the Origins of Complex Life* (London: Profile Books, 2015), 115.

9. Bruce Alberts, ed., *Molecular Biology of the Cell*, 4th ed. (New York: Garland Science, 2002). See the discussion of protein turnover in the section headed "Quality Control" in ch. 6, 557–563, esp. 558.

10. Baross, Benner, et al., 27.

11. C. Yee, W. Yang, S. Hekimi, "The Intrinsic Apoptosis Pathway Mediates the Pro-Longevity Response to Mitochondrial ROS in C. elegans," *Cell* 157, No. 4 (May 8, 2014): 897–909; Dennis Thompson, "Could Antioxidants Speed Up Cancer Progression?" *WebMD,* January 29, 2014, accessed June 26, 2017, http://www.webmd.com/cancer/news/20140129/could-antioxidants-speed-up-cancer-progression#1; Paul Offit, "The Vitamin Myth: Why We Think We Need Supplements," *The Atlantic,* July 19, 2013, accessed June 26, 2017, https://www.theatlantic.com/health/archive/2013/07/the-vitamin-myth-why-we-think-we-need-supplements/277947/.

12. Personal communication from Guillermo Gonzalez.

13. As the poet Percy Bysshe Shelley expressed the ethos, "Worlds on Worlds are Rolling over, From creation to decay, Like the bubbles on a River, Sparkling, bursting, borne away." Cited in Bertrand Russell, *History of Western Philosophy* (Oxford: Routledge, 2015), 72. For more on the idea of a multiverse, see John Leslie, *Universes* (Oxford: Routledge, 1989), and Martin J. Rees, *Just Six Numbers: The Deep Forces That Shape the Universe* (New York: Basic Books, 2000).

14. Lawrence Henderson, *The Fitness of the Environment: An Inquiry into the Biological Significance of the Properties of Matter* (New York: The Macmillan Company, 1913), 132.

15. Ball, "Will ET Drink Water?"

16. Ibid.

17. Ibid.

18. T. H. Huxley, *Evidence as to Man's Place in Nature* (New York: D. Appleton and Co., 1863), 84.

Image Credits

Introduction

By Diliff: (Own work) [CC BY-SA 3.0 (http://creativecommons.org/licenses/by-sa/3.0) or GFDL (http://www.gnu.org/copyleft/fdl.html)], via Wikimedia Commons. Source: https://en.wikipedia.org/wiki/Bridalveil_Fall#/media/File:Bridelveil_Falls_Yosemite.jpg

Chapter 1

Figure 1.1: By Kim Hansen (Own work (Own photo)) [GFDL (http://www.gnu.org/copyleft/fdl.html) or CC BY-SA 3.0 (http://creativecommons.org/licenses/by-sa/3.0)], via Wikimedia Commons

Figure 1.2: By John Evans and Howard Periman, USGS (http://ga.water.usgs.gov/edu/watercycle.html) [Public domain], via Wikimedia Commons

Chapter 2

Figure 2.1: By Saffron Blaze (Own work) [CC BY-SA 3.0 (http://creativecommons.org/licenses/by-sa/3.0)], via Wikimedia Commons

Figure 2.2: By Remi Jouan (Own work) [CC BY-SA 3.0 (http://creativecommons.org/licenses/by-sa/3.0) OR CC BY-SA 2.5 (https://creativecommons.org/licenses/by-sa/2.5/deed.en)], via Wikimedia Commons

Figure 2.3: By USGS (http://pubs.usgs.gov/publications/text/slabs.html) [Public domain], via Wikimedia Commons

Figure 2.4: By Jose F. Vigil from This Dynamic Planet -- a wall map produced jointly by the U.S. Geological Survey, the Smithsonian Institution, and the U.S. Naval Research Laboratory.

Figure 2.5: By Rob Young from United Kingdom (Þingvellir National Park, Bláskógabyggð) [CC BY 2.0 (http://creativecommons.org/licenses/by/2.0)], via Wikimedia Commons

Figure 2.6: By J. D. Griggs edit by User:Mbz1 (Own work) [Public domain], via Wikimedia Commons

Figure 2.7: By Miguel Vieira (talk · contribs) (Own work) [Public domain or Public domain], via Wikimedia Commons

Figure 2.8: By Casey Luskin. Used with permission.

Chapter 3

Figure 3.1: By Paul Harrison [GFDL (http://www.gnu.org/copyleft/fdl.html) or CC-BY-SA-3.0 (http://creativecommons.org/licenses/by-sa/3.0/)], via Wikimedia Commons

Figure 3.2: By NASA, ESA, and the Hubble Heritage Team (STScI/AURA)-ESA/ Hubble Collaboration (HubbleSite: gallery, NewsCenter) [Public domain], via Wikimedia Commons

Figure 3.3: ©NASA

Figure 3.4: By Shane.torgerson (Own work) [CC BY 3.0 (http://creativecommons. org/licenses/by/3.0)], via Wikimedia Commons

Figure 3.5: X. Cheng, T. Schulenberg, "Heat Transfer at Supercritical Pressures – Literature Review and Application to an HPLWR," Forschungszentrum Karlsruhe Technik und Umwelt, Wissenschaftliche Berichte FZKA 6609, Institute für Kern- und Energietechnik, Programm Nukleare Sicherheitsforschung, Forschungzentrum Karlsruhe GmbH, Karlsruhe, 2001. Used with permission.

Chapter 4

Figure 4.1: By Library of Congress/Benjamin Franklin [Public domain], via Wikimedia Commons

Figure 4.2: By Ytrottier [CC BY-SA 3.0 (https://creativecommons.org/licenses/by-sa/3.0/deed.en)], via Wikimedia Commons

Figure 4.3: By National Weather Service JetStream [Public domain], via Wikimedia Commons

Figure 4.4: By DWindrim (Own work) [GFDL (http://www.gnu.org/copyleft/fdl. html) or CC-BY-SA-3.0 (http://creativecommons.org/licenses/by-sa/3.0/)], via Wikimedia Commons

Figure 4.5: By Dr. Michael Pidwirny (see http://www.physicalgeography.net) [Public domain], via Wikimedia Commons

Figure 4.6: National Ocean Service, National Oceanic and Atmospheric Administration, US Department of Commerce, public domain

Chapter 5

Figure 5.1: By Webrunner (Own work) [CC BY-SA 3.0 (http://creativecommons. org/licenses/by-sa/3.0) or GFDL (http://www.gnu.org/copyleft/fdl.html)], via Wikimedia Commons

Figure 5.2: By Acroterion (Own work) [CC BY-SA 3.0 (http://creativecommons. org/licenses/by-sa/3.0) or GFDL (http://www.gnu.org/copyleft/fdl.html)], via Wikimedia Commons

Figure 5.3: By Krzysztof P. Jasiutowicz [GFDL (http://www.gnu.org/copyleft/fdl. html) or CC-BY-SA-3.0 (http://creativecommons.org/licenses/by-sa/3.0/)], via Wikimedia Commons

Figure 5.4: Kebes at English Wikipedia [CC BY-SA 3.0 (http://creativecommons. org/licenses/by-sa/3.0) or GFDL (http://www.gnu.org/copyleft/fdl.html)], via Wikimedia Commons

Figure 5.5: Kils & Marschall, 1995 [CC BY-SA 3.0 (http://creativecommons.org/licenses/by-sa/3.0) or GFDL (http://www.gnu.org/copyleft/fdl.html)], via Wikimedia Commons

Figure 5.6: Wellcome Library, London, http://wellcomeimages.org / Rene Descartes [CC BY 4.0 (http://creativecommons.org/licenses/by/4.0)], via Wikimedia Commons. https://commons.wikimedia.org/wiki/File:Descartes;_Diagram_of_ocular_refraction._Wellcome_L0012003.jpg

Chapter 6

Figure 6.1: Charles Robert Knight [Public domain], via Wikimedia Commons

Figure 6.2: By Vesalius, Andreas, 1514-1564. Andreae Vesalii Bruxellensis, scholae medicorum Patauinae professoris, suorum de humani corporis fabrica librorum epitome. Call number: HMD Collection, WZ 240 V575dhZ 1543. [Public domain], via Wikimedia Commons

Figure 6.3: By Dubaj, vectorized by Guillaume Paumier (user:guillom) (Toky.png) [Public domain], via Wikimedia Commons

Figure 6.4: By Louisa Howard [Public domain], via Wikimedia Commons

Figure 6.5: By Bibi Saint-Pol [CC BY-SA 3.0 (http://creativecommons.org/licenses/by-sa/3.0)], via Wikimedia Commons (cropped)

Chapter 7

Figure 7.1: National Park Service [Public domain] via Wikimedia Commons

Figure 7.2: By NIMSoffice [Public domain], via Wikimedia Commons

Figure 7.3: Modified from image by OpenStax College, Biology [CC BY 4.0 (https://creativecommons.org/licenses/by/4.0/)] via khanacademy.org Download OpenStax for free at http://cnx.org/contents/a4f8df82-c778-4971-8dcc-7c5c72578e94@9.

Figure 7.4: By photo taken by flickr user tanakawho (flickr) [CC BY 2.0 (http://creativecommons.org/licenses/by/2.0)], via Wikimedia Commons. Source: https://en.wikipedia.org/wiki/File:Water_drop_on_a_leaf.jpg

Chapter 8

Figure 8.1: By Brocken Inaglory (Own work) [GFDL (http://www.gnu.org/copyleft/fdl.html) or CC BY-SA 4.0-3.0-2.5-2.0-1.0 (http://creativecommons.org/licenses/by-sa/4.0-3.0-2.5-2.0-1.0)], via Wikimedia Commons

INDEX

A

Active matrix 175–177
Adams, Rachel 9
Alkahest 21, 168
Anaximander (c. 570 B.C. 30
Animal Physiology and Scaling 9
Aristotle 117
Aristotle: The Desire to Understand 117
Asimov, Isaac 159–160
Astronomy and General Physics Considered with Reference to Natural Theology (1834) 92–94

B

Ball, Philip 9, 16, 18, 55, 65, 157–158, 169, 171, 175–176, 184
Basal sliding 23
Benner, Steven 184
Bentley, Richard 15
Bicarbonate 149–155
Biocentric unity 13
Bjornerud, Marcia 9, 45, 53, 54, 57, 60, 63, 67, 69, 72, 87
Blake, Stephen 35
Blake, William 179, 182
Brady, Nyle 26
Bramwell, C. D. 129
Bridalveil Fall 11, 187
Burton, Kevin 35

C

Cambrian era 36
Campbell, I. H. 53, 122–123
Capillary water 25
Carbon dioxide 21
Carson, Rachel 37, 71
Cells, Gels, and the Engines of Life 177
Circulatory system 134–142
Clay 26–27
Clements, Paul 141
Climate and the Oceans 9

Clinical Physiology of Acid-Base and Electrolyte Disorders 150
Cold Trap (Tropopause) 81–84
Comparative Biomechanics 9
Confutation of Atheism from the Frame of the World 15
Copernican Principle 13
Cosmos 105, 118–119
Critique of Judgement 59–60
Cromie, William 103

D

Dalton, John 30
Davies, Paul 32
Deep ocean currents 101–103
De Motu Cordis 123
Discovery Institute 9
Dishoeck, Ewine van 64
Dooge, James 30

E

Earth, fire, and water 121–122
Edsall, J. T. 153
Eiseley, Loren 179, 180
Elements of Physical Oceanography 38
Encyclopaedia of Gardening 116
Erosion 20–29, 35–58
Evaporative cooling 124–127
Expansion on freezing 22–23

F

Fellgett, P. D. 129
Fire-Maker 165
Fitness of the Environment, The 9, 21, 125–126, 171
Folger, Timothy 87
Franklin, Benjamin 87
Franks, Felix 21, 168
Frisch, Wolfgang 48

G

Gaia: A New Look at Life on Earth 9, 61

Garrison, Tom 9, 89–90, 128–129
Glacier 23–24
Gonzalez, Guillermo 9
Gravitational water 25
Grotthuss mechanism 173
Gulf Stream 88–89, 100–102
Gwinnutt, Carl 141

H

H₂O: A Biography of Water 9
Hadley cell 95–98, 103–105
Haldane, J. B. S. 161
Hampton, Tyler 9
Harvey, William 123
Hasalová, Pavlina 35
Heat conduction 130–135
Henderson, Lawrence J. 9, 21, 100–
    102, 125–126, 126–128, 161, 168,
    171, 186
Himalaya Mountains 53
Holbrook, Michele 108–109
Holland, Heinrich 37
Holm, Nils 83–84
Hoyle, Fred 183
Huxley, Thomas H. 188
Hydrological cycle 31, 36
*Hydrologic Cycle and the Wisdom of
    God, The* 31
Hydrophobic force 170–171

I

Immense Journey, The 179
Introduction to Our Dynamic Planet, An
    35, 49, 50, 52

J

Jha, Alok 166, 168, 173
Johnston, Ian George 9

K

Kant, Immanuel 59–60
Kasting, James 83–84
Klemetti, Eric 47
Knauth, L. Paul 51
Kopel, Jonathan 9

L

Lane, Nick 173–174
Lear, Jonathan 117
Lenton, Tim 9, 81–82
Leonardo da Vinci 30
Levine, Xavier 97
Life of a Leaf, The 107, 110
Ling, Gilbert 177
Loudon, J. C. 116
Lovelock, James 9, 61, 63
Lunine, Jonathan 48

M

Maina, J. N. 153
Metaphysics 117
Miller, Stanley 160
Morowitz, Harold 9, 174
Mount Everest 53

N

Natural purpose 59
Nature's Destiny 112
Needham, Arthur 9, 125–126, 161,
    162–163, 166
Niagara Gorge 35
Nilsson, Anders 157
North Atlantic Drift 88, 99
North Atlantic Gyre 99

O

Ocean conveyor belt 99–103
Oceanography 9
O'Gorman, Paul 97
Olivine 45–47
Orgel, Leslie 160
Origins of Life on the Earth, The 160

P

Pacific Gyre 99
Paleocene/Eocene Temperature Maxi-
    mum (PETM) 69, 72–73
Paracelsus 175
Pettersson, Lars G. M. 157
Photosynthesis 111–113
Pilson, Michael 37
Pollack, Gerald 9, 176–177, 177

Proton Wire 173–174

R
Ray, John 31
Reading the Rocks 9, 63, 87
Revolutions that Made the Earth 9
Rogers 9
Rogers, Nick 35
Rose, Burton 150
Runaway greenhouse 72

S
Sagan, Carl 105, 118–119
Schmidt-Nielsen, Knut 9, 134
Schneider, Tapio 97
Silicon homeostat 73–75
Soil 24–29
Specific heat 127–134
Stromatolite 61–62
Surface tension 22–23
Szent-Györgyi, Albert 17, 175

T
Tanford, Charles 171
Taylor, S. R. 53, 122–123
Tectonic Plates 41–47
Tectonic recycling 63
Thermal inertia 89–90, 128–129
Tuan, Yi-Fu 30
Twain, Mark 90

U
Uniqueness of Biological Materials, The 9, 125–126

V
Vallis, Geoffrey 9
Viscosity 22, 172–173
Vogel, Steven 9, 107, 110, 138–139, 143–144
Voltaire 57

W
Wadham, Peter 115–116
Wald, George 9, 105–107, 159–160
Water
  Cellular life 157–183
  Climate moderation 89
  Expansion on freezing 76
  Freezing from top 76–81
  Greenhouse gas 82–83
  High heat capacity 77
  Lateral heat 77–78, 90–92
  Low heat conductivity 78
  Sea water 78–81
  States of 16–17, 31
  Surface tension 105–111
  Transparency 113–118
  Viscosity 29, 31, 78
Water and the Cell 9, 176
Water cycle 18–20
Water Encyclopedia, The 49
Watson, Andrew J. 9, 81–82
Weathering 20–29
Wegener, Alfred 44
Weil, Raymond 26
Weinberg, Roberto 35
Wells, Jonathan 9
West, John 9
Whewell, William 92–94, 117–118
Widdowson, Mike 35
Wisdom of God Manifest in the Works of Creation 31
Wise, Donald 83
Witt, Jonathan 9
Wyman, J. 153

Y
Yosemite 11, 187

Z
Zwieniecki, Maciej 108–109

Printed in Great Britain
by Amazon

34579029R00128